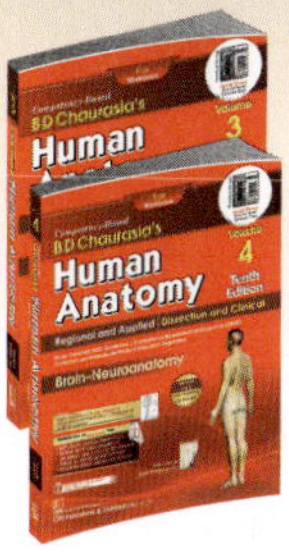

Given free with
BD Chaurasia's
Human Anatomy, Vols 3&4

Created by Yogesh Sontakke

Mind Maps in Anatomy

Head, Neck and Neuroanatomy

Thyroid Gland

Shield-like, endocrine gland situated in lower part of the front and sides of the neck.

Features

Parts

Two lobes, Isthmus, Pyramidal lobe

Location

In neck: C5–C7, T1 level
Extent: From oblique line of thyroid cartilage to 5th tracheal ring

Dimensions

Weight: 25 g, Lobe: 5 x 2 x 2 cm, Isthmus: 1.25 x 1.25 cm

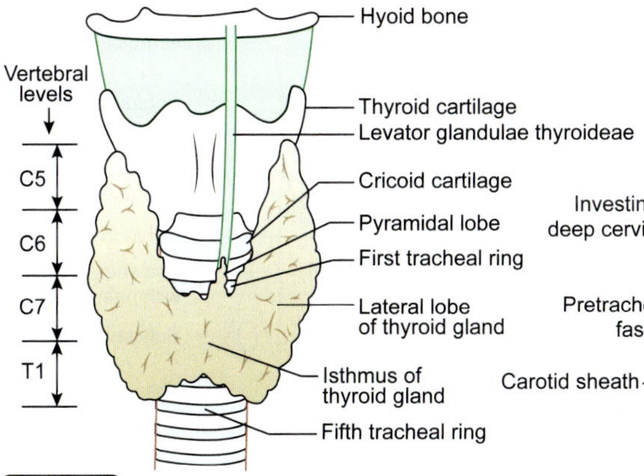

Capsules

Inner true capsule, Outer false capsule
Capillary plexus lies deep to true capsule

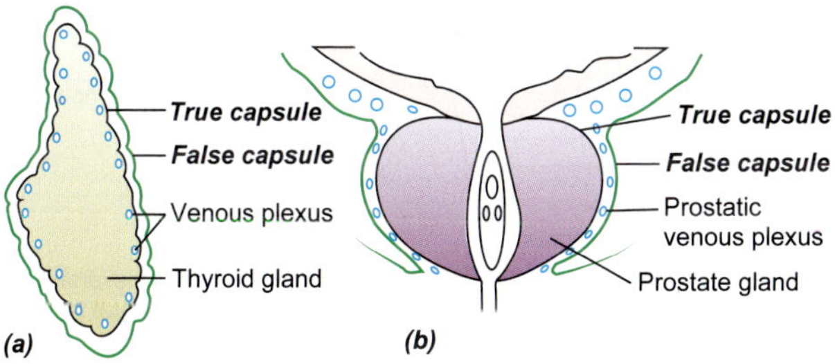

Capsules of the thyroid and prostate glands and venous plexuses

Histology

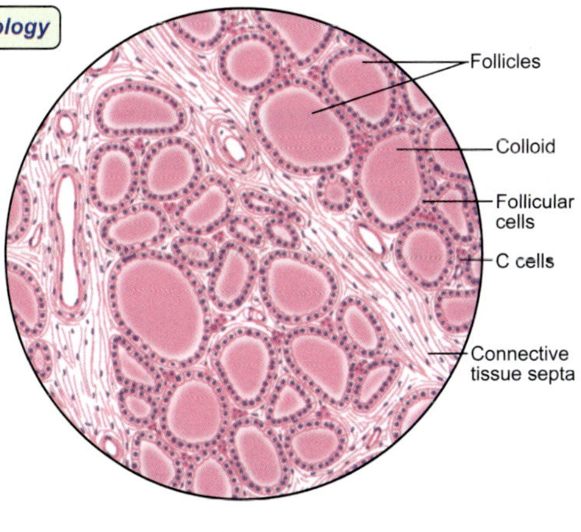

Lobe and its relations

Apex: Directed upward;
Lies between sternothyroid and inferior constrictor

Base: Extends up to 5th tracheal ring
Closely related to inferior thyroid artery and recurrent laryngeal nerve

Surfaces

Lateral: Convex, Covered by SCM, Sternohyoid, Superior belly of omohyoid, Sternothyroid
Medial: Related to: Trachea, Oesophagus, Inferior constrictor, Cricothyroid, Cricoid and thyroid cartilages, External laryngeal and recurrent laryngeal nerves
Posterolateral: Related to: Carotid sheath

Borders

Anterior: Thin, Related to: Anterior branches of superior thyroid artery
Posterior: Rounded, Related to: Inferior thyroid artery, Arterial anastomosis, Parathyroid glands, Thoracic duct (on left)

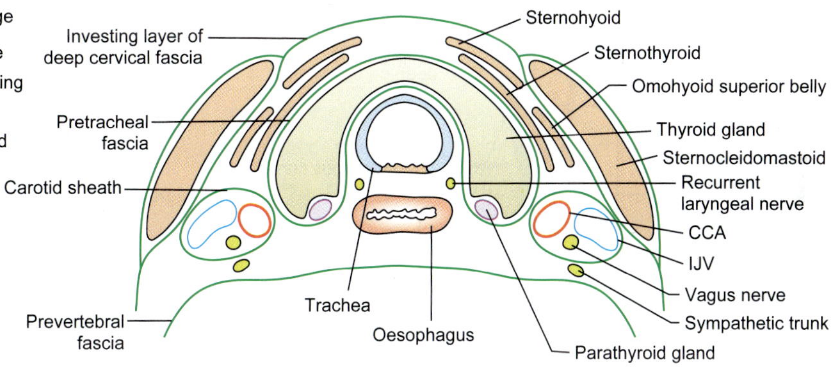

Blood supply

Arteries

Superior thyroid, Inferior thyroid, Thyroidea ima artery
Accessory thyroid arteries

Venous drainage

Superior thyroid → IJV; Middle thyroid → IJV
Inferior thyroid → Brachiocephalic vein; Fourth thyroid (Kocher's) → IJV

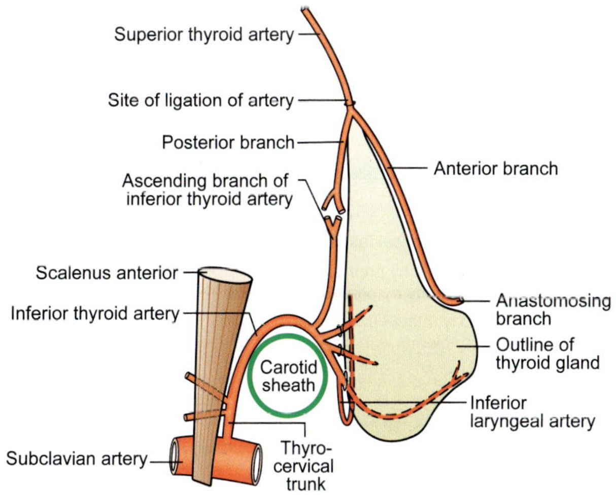

Illuminating the young minds

AF516639

Posterior Triangle of Neck

A space on the side of neck situated behind sternocleidomastoid muscle

Boundaries

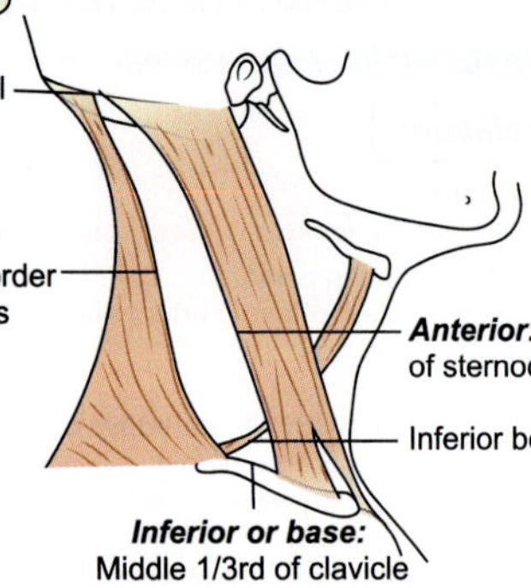

Roof

Skin, Superficial fascia
Platysma,
External and posterior jugular veins
Great auricular, transverse cervical, supraclavicular, lesser occipital nerves
Investing layer of deep cervical fascia

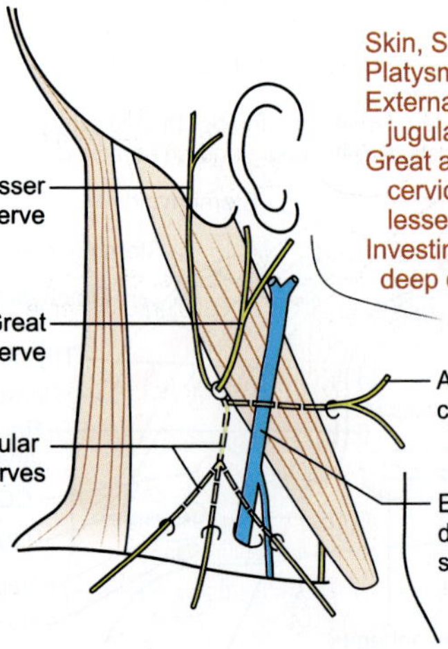

Floor

Prevertebral fascia, Semispinalis capitis
Splenius capitis, Levator scapulae, Scalenus medius

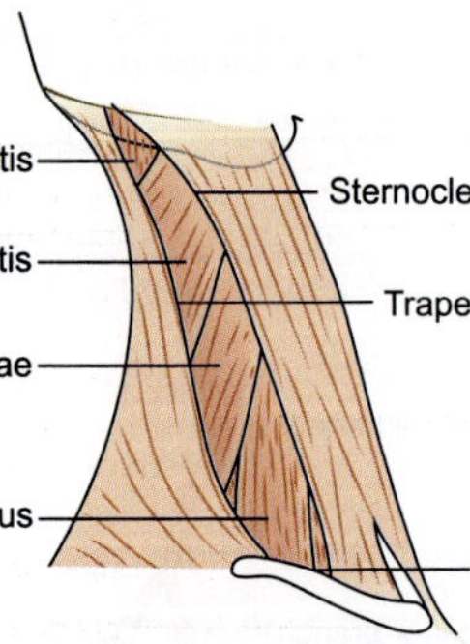

Content Divided by inferior belly of omohyoid into

Occipital triangle

XI nerve, Great auricular, Transverse cervical, Supraclavicular and lesser occipital nerves, Dorsal scapular nerve
Branches from C3 and C4, Transverse cervical artery and vein
Occipital artery, Occipital nodes

Supraclavicular (subclavian triangle)

Roots and trunks of brachial plexus, Nerve to serratus anterior
Nerve to subclavius, Suprascapular nerve, Third part of subclavian artery, Subclavian vein, Suprascapular artery and vein
Transverse cervical artery and vein, External jugular vein
Supraclavicular nodes

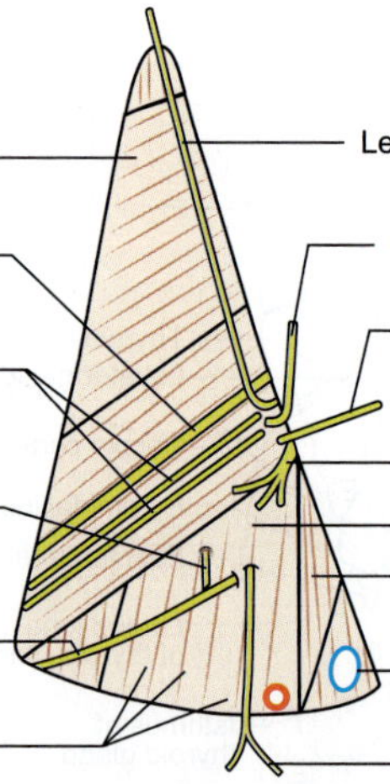

(a)

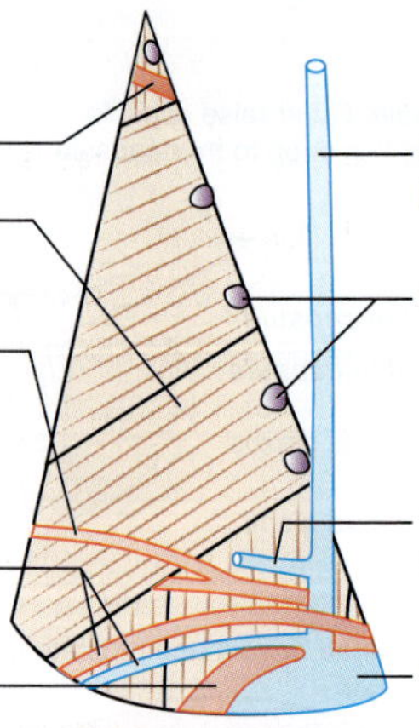

(b)

Carotid Sheath

Derivative of deep cervical fascia

Formation: Anteriorly by pretracheal fascia;
Posteriorly by prevertebral fascia

Extent: Superiorly attached to the base of skull;
Inferiorly blends with arch of aorta in superior mediastinum

Contents: Common and internal carotid arteries, Internal jugular vein, Vagus nerve

Relations: Anterior: Ansa cervicalis, SCM
Posterior: Cervical sympathetic chain, Prevertebral fascia

Clinical integration:

Carotid sheath – thin around vein → Permits venous return

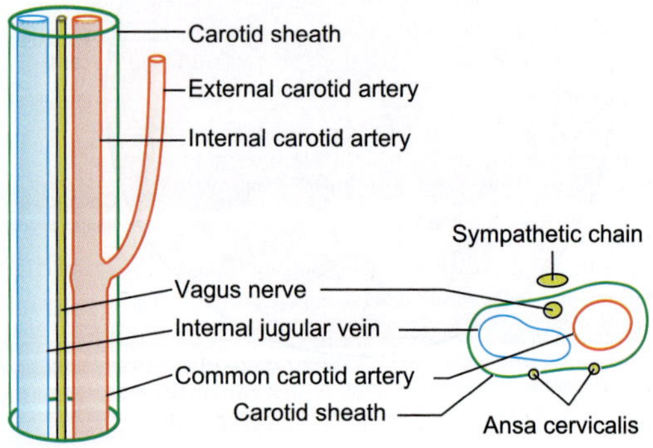

Extraocular Muscles

	Recti muscles	Oblique muscles: Superior oblique	Oblique muscles: Inferior oblique	Levator palpebrae superioris
	Four: Superior, medial, inferior, lateral			
Origin:	Common annular tendinous ring	Body of sphenoid, superomedial to optic canal	Orbital surface of maxilla	Lesser wing of sphenoid anterior to optic canal
Insertion:	On sclera, posterior to limbus, in front of equator of eyeball	On sclera, behind the equator of eyeball, in posterosuperior quadrant	On sclera, behind the equator of eyeball, in posteroinferior quadrant	Superior lamina - skin of upper eyelid - anterior surface of tarsal plate Inferior lamina forms ***superior tarsal*** muscle

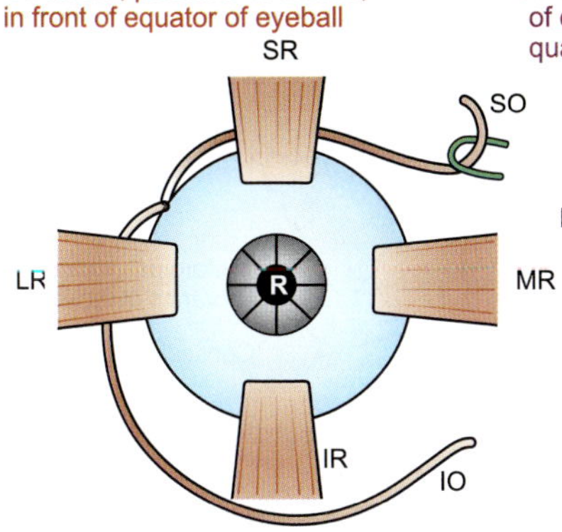

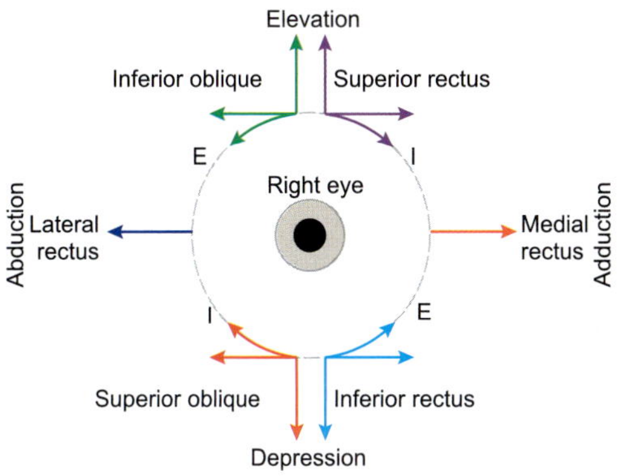

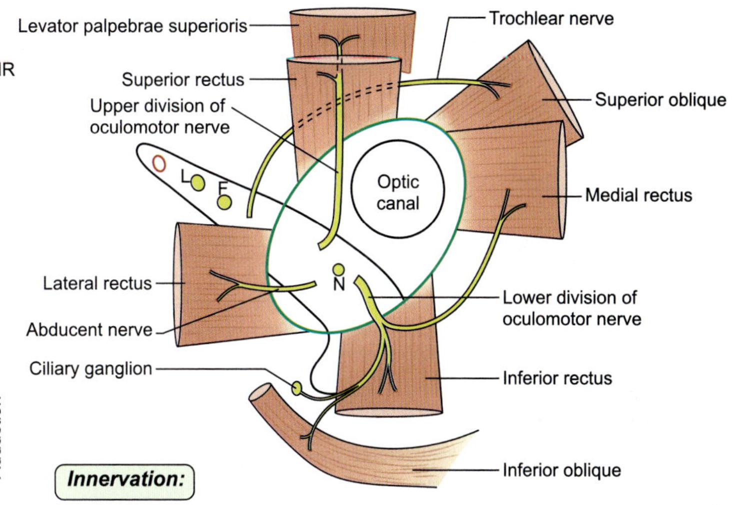

Innervation:

All voluntary extraocular muscles are supplied by oculomotor nerve except LR6 (lateral rectus – abducent nerve) and SO4 (Superior oblique – trochlear nerve)

BDC yogesh

Scalp

Tissue covering the skull

Extent

Anterior: Supraorbital margin
Posterior: External occipital protuberance, superior nuchal line
On each side: Zygomatic arch

Layers

Skin

Hairy; Adherent to epicranial aponeurosis
Numerous hair follicles and sebaceous glands

Subcutaneous connective tissue

Superficial fascia; Dense connective tissue; Passage for blood vessels and nerves

Epicranial aponeurosis

Called galea aponeurotica; Gives insertion to frontalis and occipitalis

Loose areolar tissue

Anteriorly extends into the upper eyelid
Posteriorly extends up to superior nuchal line
Gives passage to emissary vein

Pericranium

Periosteum of cranial bones; Loosely attached to bones

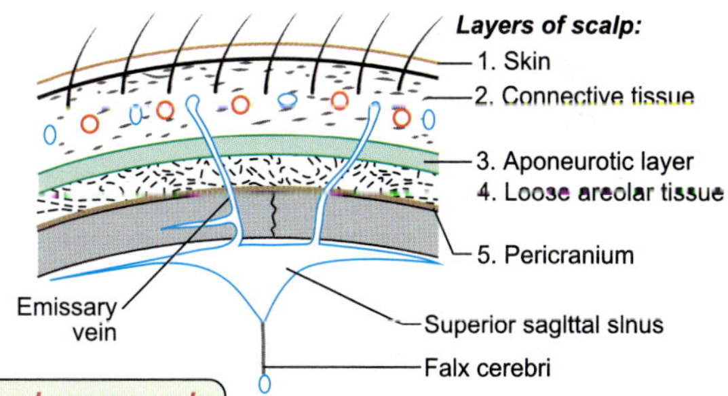

Arterial and nerve supply

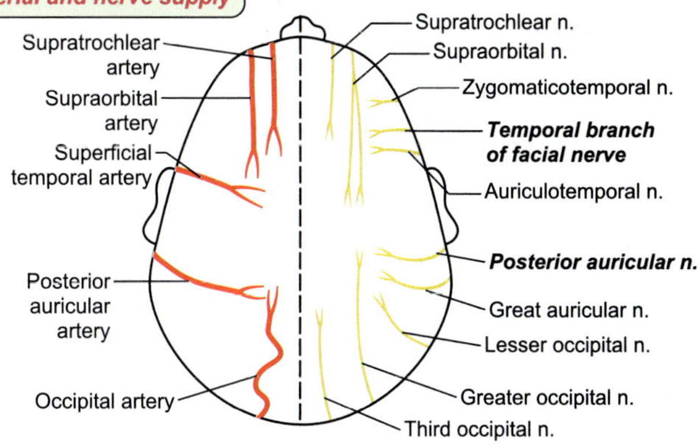

Clinical integration

Sebaceous cyst, surgical layers of scalp, black eye, dangerous area of scalp, safety-valve haematoma, cephalohaematoma, caput succedaneum, scalp wound bleeding, gaping wound of scalp.

Parotid Gland

The parotid gland is the largest of the salivary glands
(Para = around; otic = ear)

Capsule of parotid gland

Formed by investing layer of deep cervical fascia
Has two laminae:
a. Superficial lamina is thick, strong, unyielding and adherent to the glands
b. Deep lamina is thin

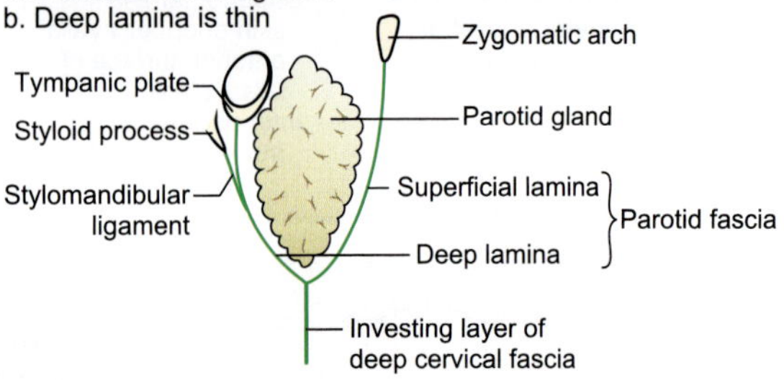

External features

Apex: Directed downward, Related to posterior belly of digastric

Base: Superior surface
Relations: 1. External acoustic meatus, 2. TMJ

Surfaces

- ***Superficial:*** Relations: Skin, Superficial fascia with great auricular nerve, Platysma, Superficial lamina of parotid fascia
- ***Anteromedial:*** Relations: Masseter, Ramus of mandible Medial pterygoid, Temporomandibular joint, Emerging branches of facial nerve, Emerging maxillary artery
- ***Posteromedial:*** Relations: Mastoid process, Sternocleidomastoid Posterior belly of digastric, Styloid apparatus, Internal carotid artery, Internal jugular vein, Last four cranial nerves

Borders: Anterior, Posterior, Medial

Structures emerging from the parotid gland

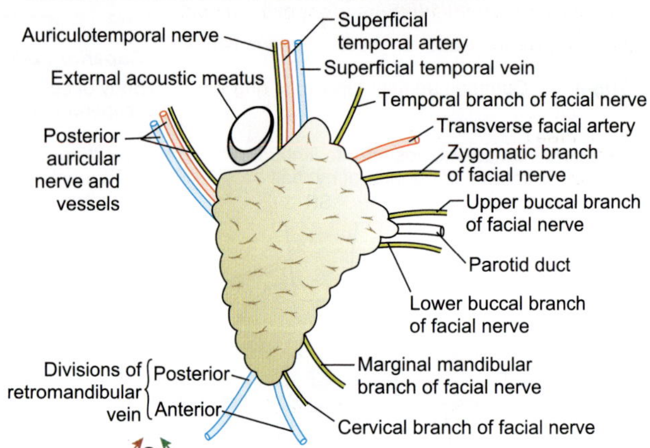

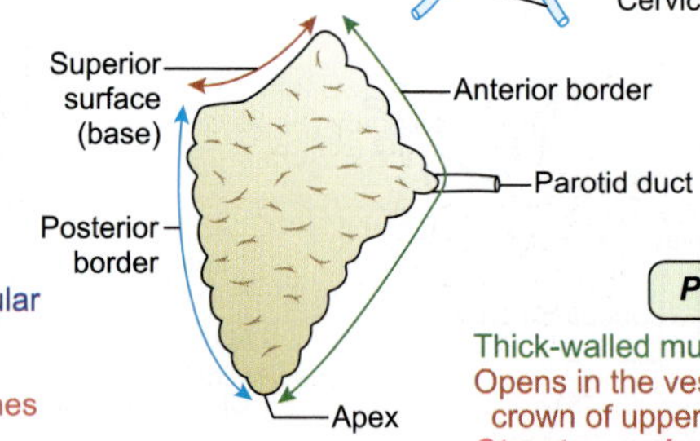

Parotid duct

Thick-walled mucomuscular tube, 5 cm long
Opens in the vestibule of mouth opposite the crown of upper 2nd molar teeth
Structures pierced: Buccal pad of fat, Buccopharyngeal fascia, Buccinator, Oral mucosa

Relations

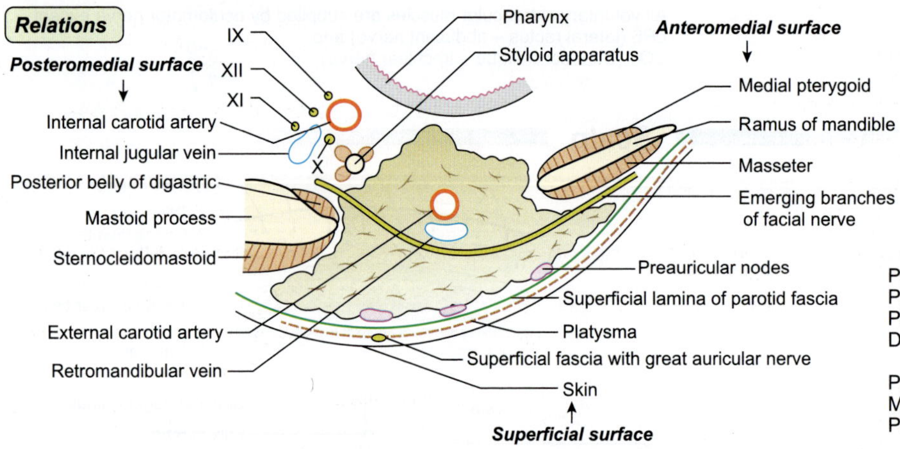

Nerve supply

Parasympathetic:
Secretomotor, from otic ganglion

Sympathetic:
Vasomotor, from T1 segment of spinal cord

Sensory:
Auriculotemporal nerve
Great auricular nerve

Clinical integration

Palpation of parotid duct
Parotid sialography
Parotid abscess
Drainage of parotid abscess by horizontal incision (Hilton's method)
Parotidectomy (Removal of parotid gland)
Mixed parotid tumour
Parotid calculi

Structures within the parotid gland

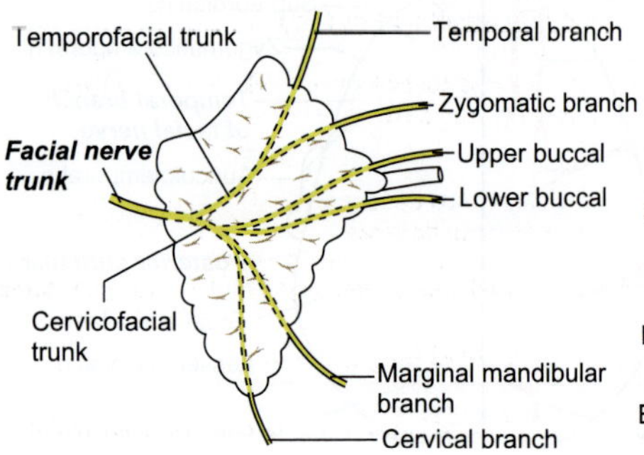

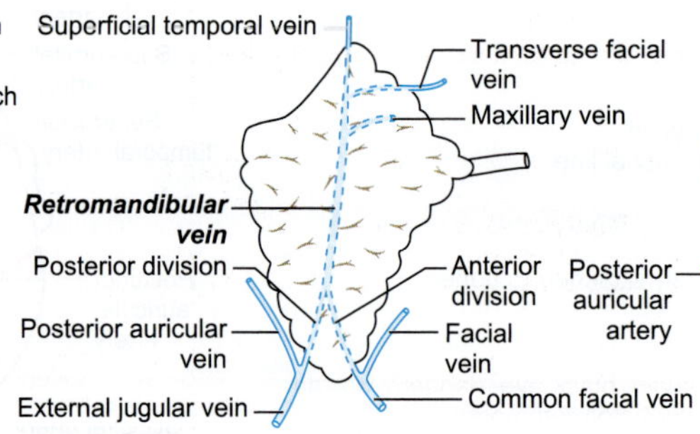

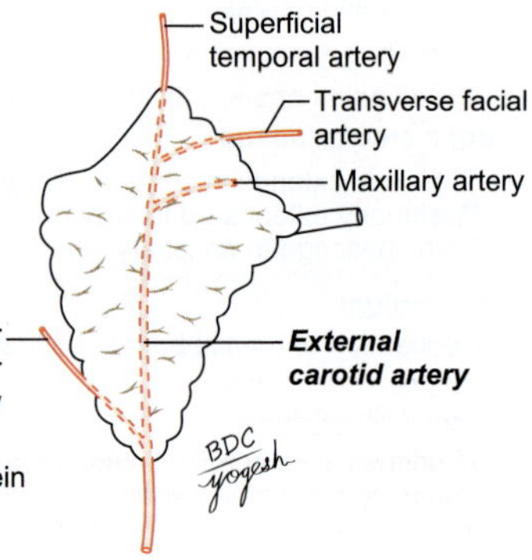

Tongue

Muscular organ situated in the floor of the mouth.

External features

Root: Fixed, attached to styloid process, palate, mandible, hyoid bone

Tip: Free anterior end

Body

Dorsal surface

V-shaped sulcus terminalis divides it into:
- A. Oral part: Median furrow, Papillae
- B. Pharyngeal part: Lingual tonsils, Foramen caecum

Posteriormost part: Connected to epiglottis, Median and two lateral glossoepiglottic folds

Ventral surface: Frenulum linguae, Deep lingual veins Plica fimbriata

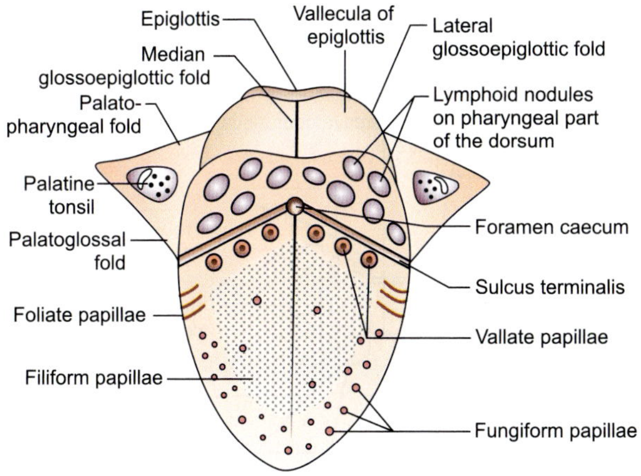

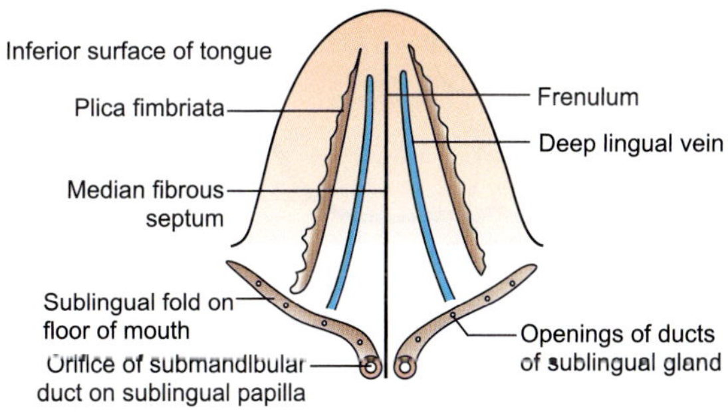

Papillae of tongue

Surface projections

Filiform: Most numerous, Smallest, Minute conical projections No taste buds

Fungiform: Mushroom-shaped, Small pink spots Contains apical taste buds

Circumvallate: 8–12 papillae, Dome-shaped, Located anterior to suclus terminalis Contains lateral wall taste buds

Foliate: Parallel rows of ridges near the margin of tongue Rudimentary, No taste buds

Muscles of tongue

Intrinsic muscles

Lie within the tongue, Change the shape of tongue
1. Superior longitudinal, 2. Inferior longitudinal
3. Transverse, 4. Vertical

Extrinsic muscles

Connect tongue to styloid process, palate, mandible or hyoid bone
Move the tongue, Change the position of tongue
1. Genioglossus 2. Hyoglossus
3. Styloglossus 4. Palatoglossus

All supplied by hypoglossal nerve except palatoglossus (supplied by cranial root of accessory nerve)

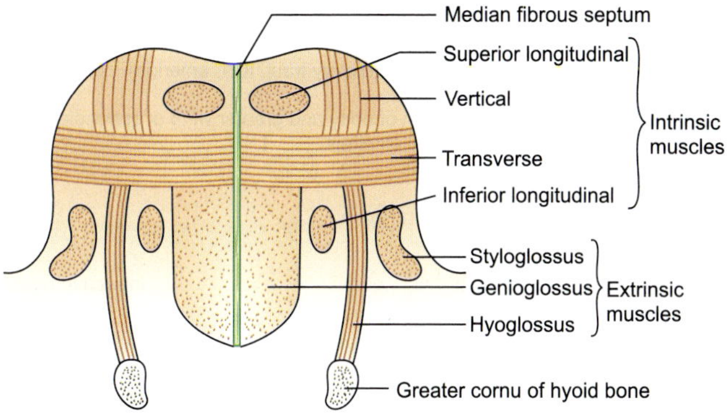

Lymphatic drainage

Marginal vessels: Drain marginal area of anterior part of tongue to:
- Submental LN, Submandibular LN, Jugulo-omohyoid LN
- Digastric LN

Central vessels: Drain central region of anterior 2/3rds of tongue to:
- Jugulodigastric LN, Jugulo-omohyoid LN

Dorsal vessels: Drain circumvallate papillae and posterior 1/3rd of tongue to: - Jugulodigastric LN, Jugulo-omohyoid LN

Note: Lymphatics from the tip and the central part of tongue drain bilaterally.

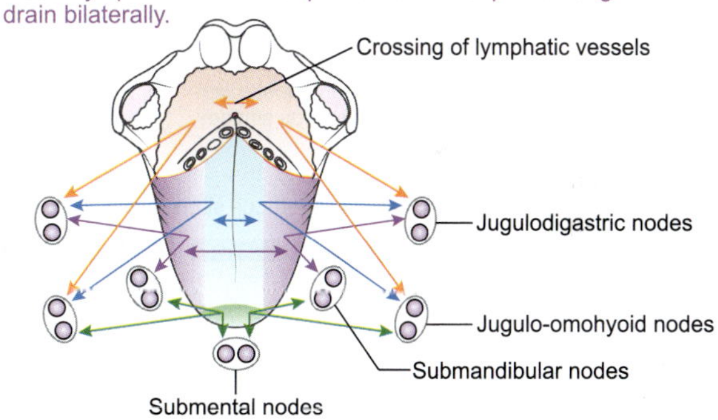

Nerve supply of tongue

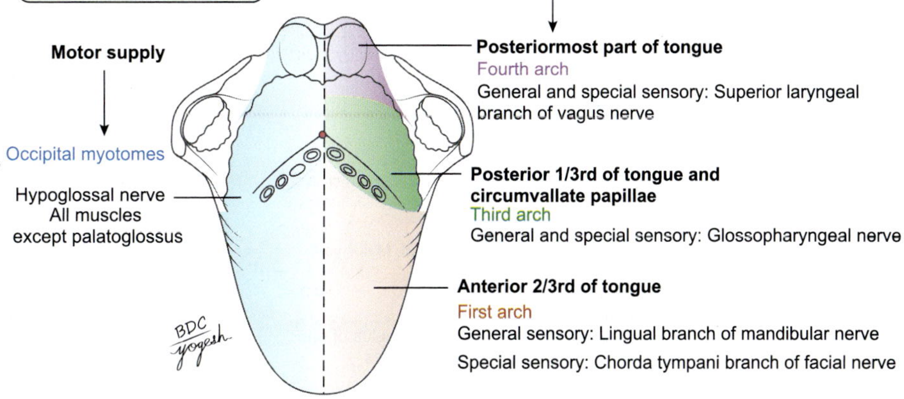

Cavernous Sinus

A large dural venous sinus that lies between the two layers of the dura mater
Size: 2 x 1 cm

Location

In middle cranial fossa, On either side of body of sphenoid

Parts

Roof and lateral wall: Formed by meningeal layer of dura mater
Floor and medial wall: Formed by endosteal layer of dura mater

Extent

Anteriorly: Up to superior orbital fissure
Posteriorly: Up to apex of petrous temporal bone

Relations

Superior: Optic chiasma, optic tract, olfactory tract, ICA, anterior perforated sub.
Inferior: Foramen lacerum, junction of body and greater wing of sphenoid
Medial: Pituitary gland, sphenoidal air sinus
Laterally: Temporal lobe with uncus
Anteriorly: Superior orbital fissure
Posteriorly: Petrous part of temporal bone

Structures in wall

Within lateral wall: Oculomotor nerve, Trochlear nerve, Ophthalmic nerve
Passing through sinus: ICA, Abducent nerve

Tributaries

Superior ophthalmic vein, Inferior ophthalmic vein, Central vein of retina, Superficial middle cerebral vein, Inferior cerebral veins, Sphenoparietal sinus, Frontal trunk of middle meningeal vein

Communications

Transverse sinus ↔ Superior petrosal sinus
Internal jugular vein ↔ Inferior petrosal sinus
Pterygoid venous plexus ↔ Emissary veins
Facial vein ↔ Superior ophthalmic vein, emissary veins
Superior sagittal sinus ↔ Superficial middle cerebral vein, superior anastomotic vein
Internal vertebral venous plexus ↔ Basilar venous plexus
Opposite cavernous sinus ↔ Anterior and posterior intercavernous sinuses

Clinical integration

Cavernous sinus thrombosis, carotid-cavernous sinus fistula

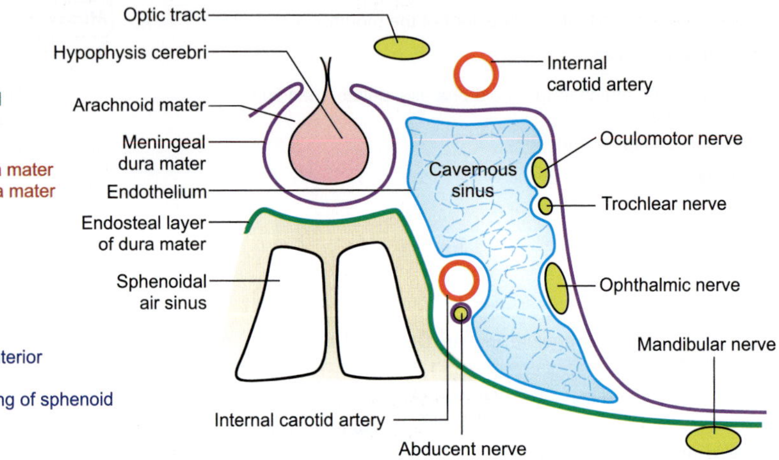

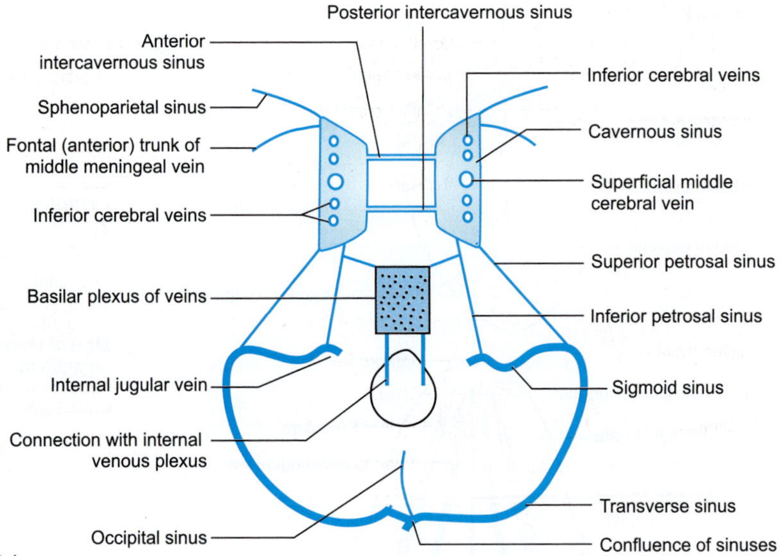

Temporomandibular Joint

Complex, Bicondylar, Synovial joint

Articular surface

Superior: Temporal bone: Articular fossa, Articular eminence
Inferior: Head of mandible

Joint cavity

Two compartments: Upper menisco-temporal, Lower menisco-mandibular

Articular disc

Oval fibrocartilage, Degenerated tendon of lateral pterygoid
Superior convex, Inferior concavoconvex surfaces

Blood supply: Maxillary artery, Superficial temporal artery
Lymphatics: Superficial parotid, Deep parotid, Upper deep cervical
Nerve supply: Auriculo-temporal, Masseteric

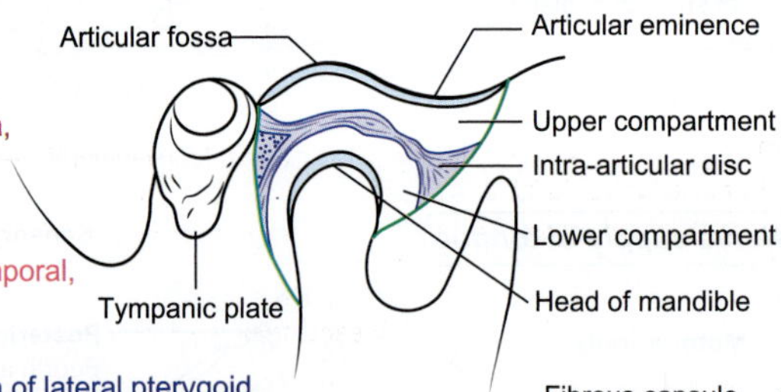

Ligaments:
Capsule
Lateral temporomandibular
Sphenomandibular
Stylomandibular
Pterygomandibular

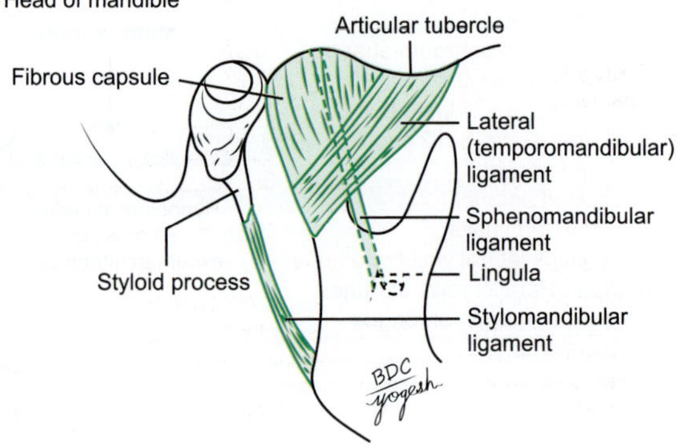

Movements of TMJ and the responsible muscles

Depression: Lateral pterygoid, Gravity, Digastric, Geniohyoid, Mylohyoid
Elevation: Masseter, Medial pterygoid, Temporalis
Protrusion: Medial and lateral pterygoid
Retraction: Posterior fibres of temporalis
Side-by-side or chewing movements: Medial and lateral pterygoids of one side contracting alternately with that of contralateral side muscles

Palate

Hard palate Partition between the nasal and oral cavities

Bony formation

- Maxilla, Palatine bone
Cruciform suture
Posterior border: Palatine aponeurosis
Posterior nasal spine: Musculus uvulae
Palatine crest: Tensor veli palatini

Foramina

Incisive canal: Greater palatine vessels and nerve,
Nasopalatine nerve
Greater palatine foramen: Greater palatine vessels and nerve
Lesser palatine foramina: Lesser palatine nerves and vessels

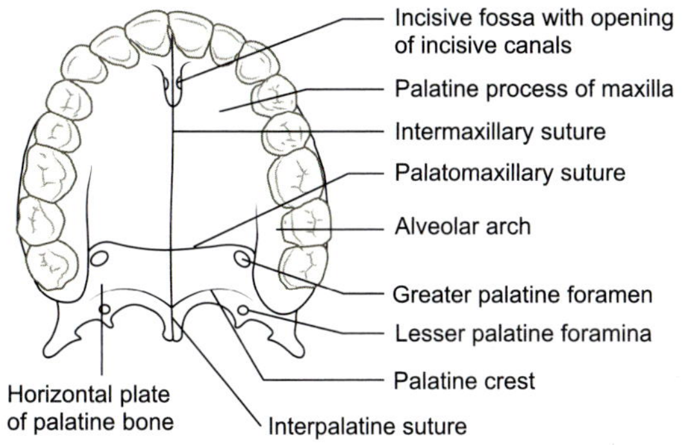

Soft palate Movable mucomuscular flap

External features

Two surfaces: Anterior (oral): Median raphe, Posterior
Two borders: Superior, inferior (free)
Two mucosal arches: Palatoglossal, palatopharyngeal

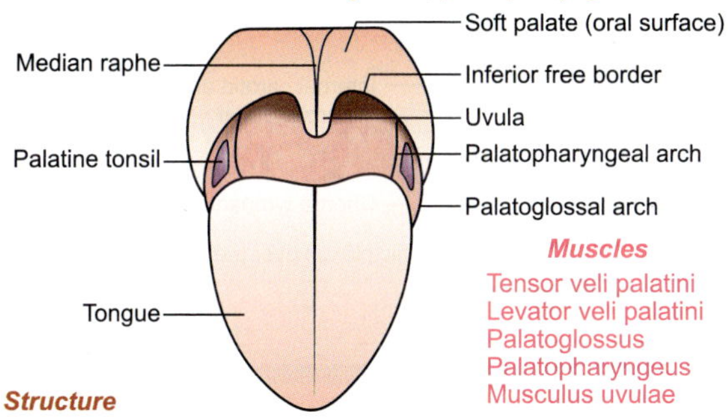

Muscles

Tensor veli palatini
Levator veli palatini
Palatoglossus
Palatopharyngeus
Musculus uvulae

Structure

Mucosa
Posterior surface: Pseudostratified ciliated columnar epithelium
Anterior surface: Nonkeratinized stratified squamous epithelium
Submucosa, Palatine aponeurosis, Muscles

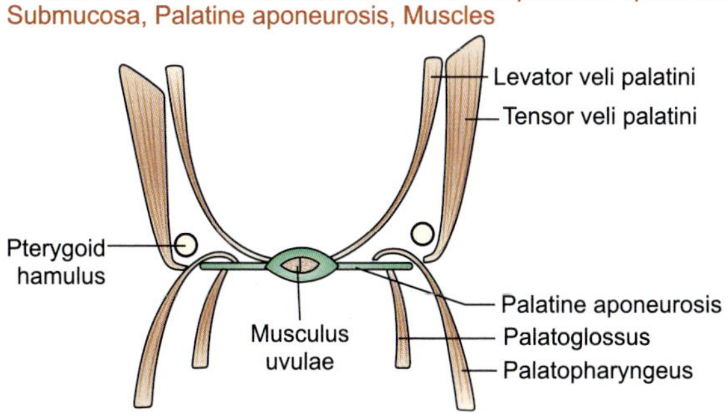

Nerve supply

Motor: All muscles by cranial root of accessory nerve except tensor veli palatini (by mandibular nerve)
General sensation: Glossopharyngeal, lesser palatine nerves
Taste sensation: Lesser palatine nerve
Secretomotor: Pterygopalatine ganglion

Palatine Tonsil

Almond-shaped mass

Location

In the lateral wall of oropharynx

Tonsillar fossa: Boundaries:
- Anterior: Palatoglossal arch
- Posterior: Palatopharyngeal arch
- Apex: Soft palate
- Base: Posterior 1/3rd of tongue

Tonsillar bed Pharyngobasillar fascia, Superior constrictor
Buccopharyngeal fascia, Styloglossus
Glossopharyngeal nerve

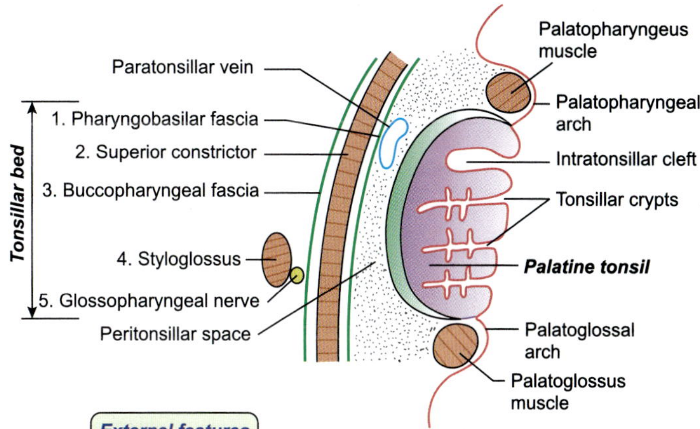

External features

Medial surface: Free,
Lined by nonkeratinized stratified squamous epithelium
Tonsillar pits (12–15), Tonsillar crypts, Intratonsillar cleft
Lateral surface - covered by capsule
Anterior border - related to palatoglossal arch
Posterior border - related to palatopharyngeal arch
Upper pole: Reach soft palate
Lower pole: Suspensory ligament of tonsil

Supply

Arterial supply

- Tonsillar branches of facial artery, Ascending palatine branch of facial art.
- Dorsal lingual branches of lingual artery
- Ascending pharyngeal branches of external carotid artery
- Greater palatine branches of maxillary artery

Venous drainage: Paratonsillar vein, Pharyngeal plexus
Lymphatic drainage: Jugulodigastric nodes
Innervation

- Glossopharyngeal nerve, Greater and lesser palatine branches of pterygopalatine ganglion

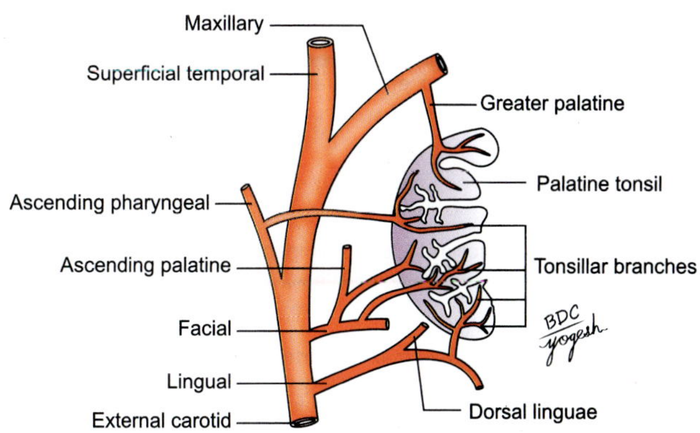

Clinical anatomy

Tonsillitis, Tonsillectomy, Quinsy
Ear pain in tonsillitis, Postoperative haemorrhage in tonsillectomy

Middle Ear

Definition
Tympanic cavity,
Narrow slit within the petrous part of temporal bone

Measurement
Vertical: 15 mm Anteroposterior: 15 mm
Transverse: 6 mm at roof, 2 mm in centre, 4 mm at floor

Communication
Anteriorly with nasopharynx through auditory tube
Posteriorly with mastoid antrum through aditus to antrum

Contents
Air, Ear ossicles, Chorda tympani, Tympanic plexus
Muscles: Tensor tympani, Stapedius

Clinical integration
Otitis media, chronic suppurative otitis media.

Boundaries of middle ear

Roof: Tegmental wall, Formed by tegmen tympani
Continue: Anteriorly as roof of canal for tensor tympani
Posteriorly as roof of mastoid antrum

Floor: Jugular wall, Formed by thin, convex plate of temporal bone
Separates from superior bulb of, IJV
Tympanic canaliculus for tympanic branch of glossopharyngeal nerve

Lateral wall: Tympanic membrane, Temporal bone in epitympanum
Petrotympanic fissure, Anterior canal for chorda tympani nerve

Medial wall: Labyrinthine wall, Promontory, Oval window, Round window,
Sinus tympani, Prominence of facial canal,
Prominence of lateral semicircular canal

Anterior wall: Narrow, Openings of canal for tensor tympani, auditory tube
Bony plate separates it from carotid canal, Processus cochleariformis

Posterior wall: Aditus to mastoid antrum, Pyramid: Origin of stapedius
Vertical part of facial canal, Posterior canaliculus for chorda tympani,
Fossa incudis

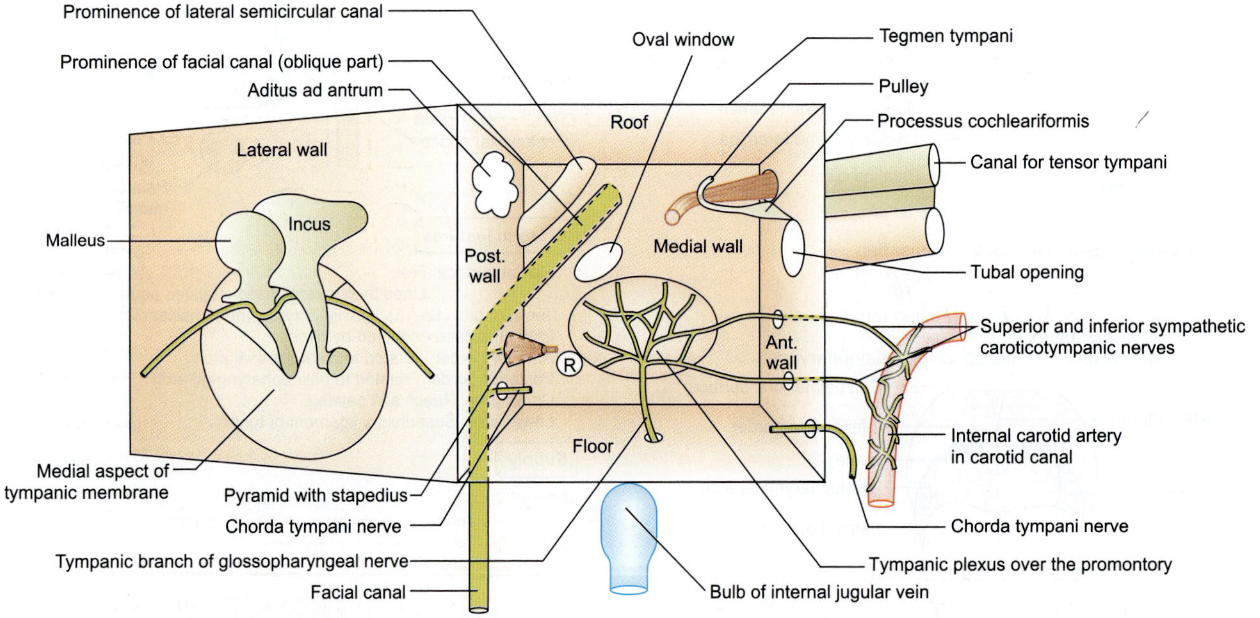

Tympanic Membrane (eardrum)

Oval semitransparent membrane,
Separates external ear from middle ear, Size: 8 mm diameter

Position
Placed obliquely, 55° angle with floor of external acoustic meatus
Looks downward, forward, and laterally
In newborn: Lies horizontally

Structure
Outer cuticular layer (skin), Middle fibrous layer
Inner mucosal layer, Umbo – point of maximum convexity

Parts
Pars tensa, Pars flaccida, Annulus tympanicus
Anterior and posterior malleolar folds

Blood supply
Arterial supply
- Deep auricular branch of maxillary artery
- Anterior tympanic branch of maxillary artery
- Posterior tympanic branch of stylomastoid artery
Venous drainage: External jugular vein, Transverse sinus

Innervation
Outer surface: Auriculotemporal branches of vagus nerve
- Auricular branch of vagus nerve
Inner surface: Tympanic branch of glossopharyngeal nerve

Clinical integration: Clinical examination, otoscopy, myringotomy

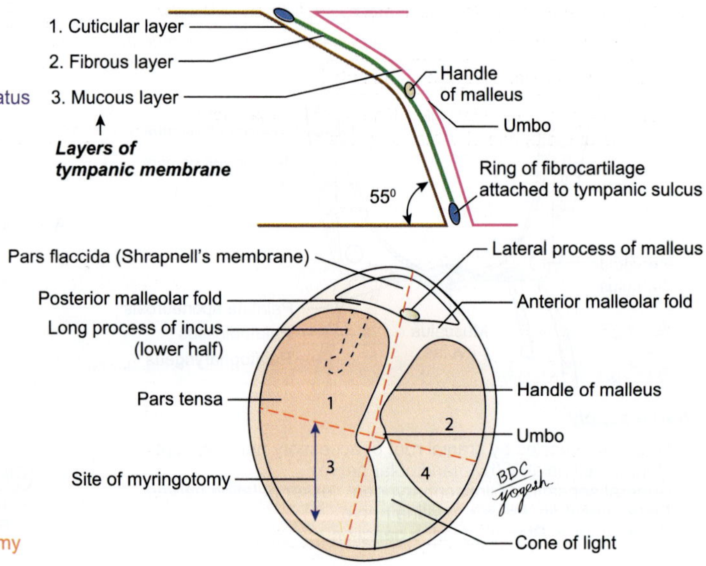

Muscles of Mastication

The principal muscles of the mastication are as follows:
1. Masseter, 3. Lateral pterygoid, 2. Temporalis, 4. Medial pterygoid.

Masseter

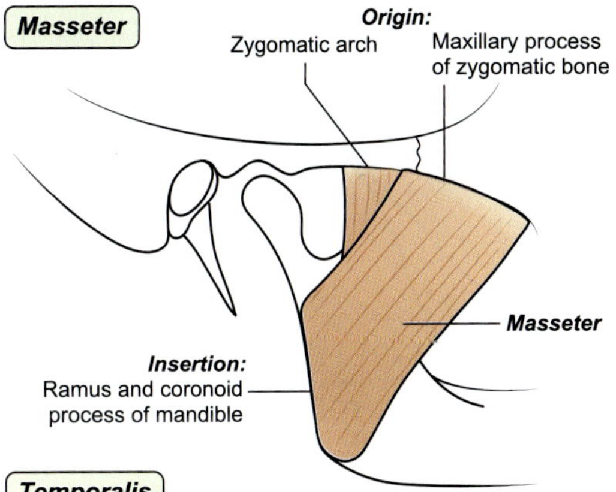

Temporalis

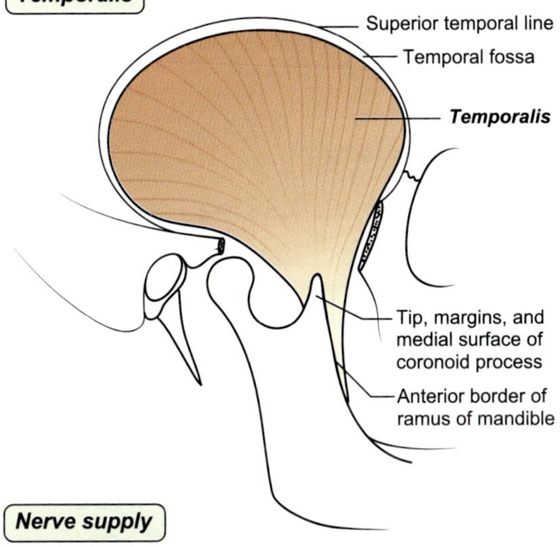

Nerve supply

Masseter: Masseteric nerve, a branch of anterior division of mandibular nerve

Temporalis: Two deep temporal branches from anterior division of mandibular nerve

Lateral pterygoid: A branch from anterior division of mandibular nerve

Medial pterygoid: Nerve to medial pterygoid, branch of the main trunk of mandibular nerve

Relation of lateral pterygoid muscle

Superficial relations: Masseter, Ramus of the mandible
Tendon of the temporalis, Maxillary artery

Deep relations: Mandibular nerve, Middle meningeal artery
Sphenomandibular ligament, Deep head of the medial pterygoid

Structures emerging at the upper border
Deep temporal nerves, Masseteric nerve

Structures emerging at the lower border
Lingual nerve, Inferior alveolar nerve and artery
Middle meningeal and accessory meningeal arteries pass upwards deep to it

Structures passing through the gap between the two heads
The maxillary artery enters the gap
The buccal branch of the mandibular nerve with buccal artery comes out through the gap
The pterygoid plexus of veins surrounds the lateral pterygoid.

Lateral pterygoid

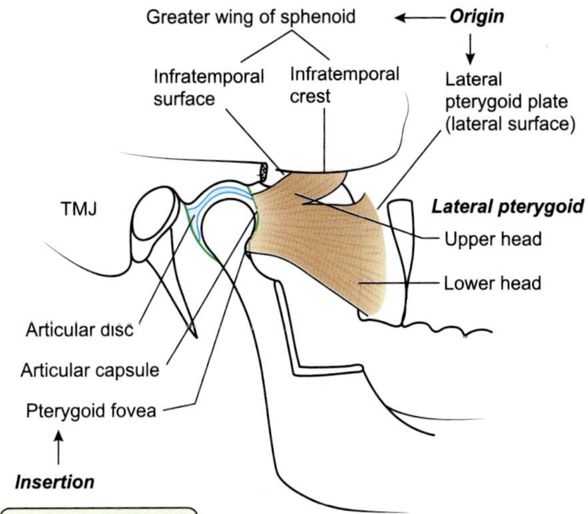

Medial pterygoid

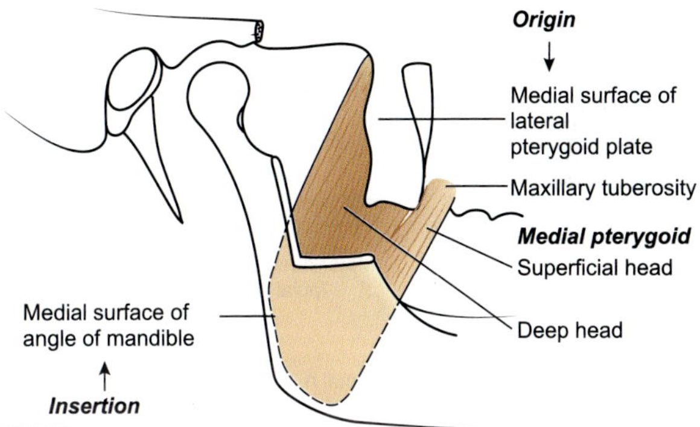

Actions

Masseter: a. Elevates mandible to close the mouth to bite
b. Superficial fibres cause protrusion

Temporalis: Elevates mandible; Helps in side-to-side grinding movement; Posterior fibres retract the protruded mandible

Lateral pterygoid: Depress mandible to open mouth, with suprahyoid muscles. It is indispensable for actively opening the mouth; Protrudes mandible; Right lateral pterygoid turns the chin to left side

Medial pterygoid: Elevates mandible; Helps protrude mandible; Right medial pterygoid with right lateral pterygoid turn the chin to left side as part of grinding movements

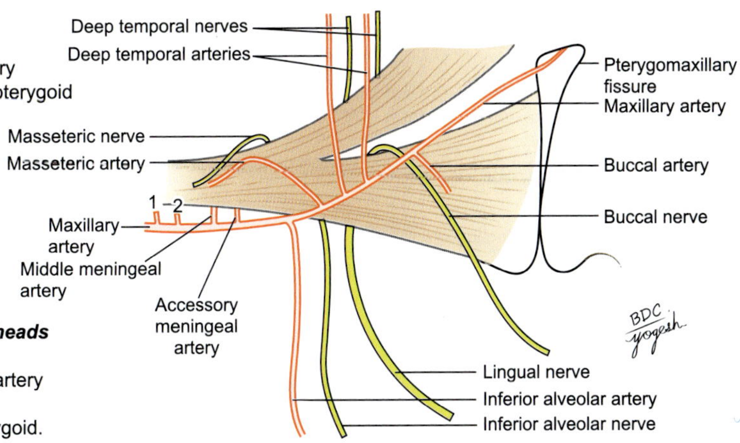

Facial Nerve

Nerve of second branchial arch,
Supplies mainly muscles of facial expressions

Functional components and nuclei of facial nerve

- ***SVE:*** Motor nucleus of facial nerve, Supplies muscles of 2nd pharyngeal arch
- ***GVE:*** Lacrimatory nucleus → Parasympathetic to lacrimal gland
  Superior salivatory nucleus → Parasympathetic to submandibular and sublingual glands
- ***SVA:*** Nucleus tractus solitarius, Taste sensation from anterior 2/3rds of tongue except vallate papillae
- ***GSA:*** Spinal nucleus of trigeminal nerve for skin of external ear

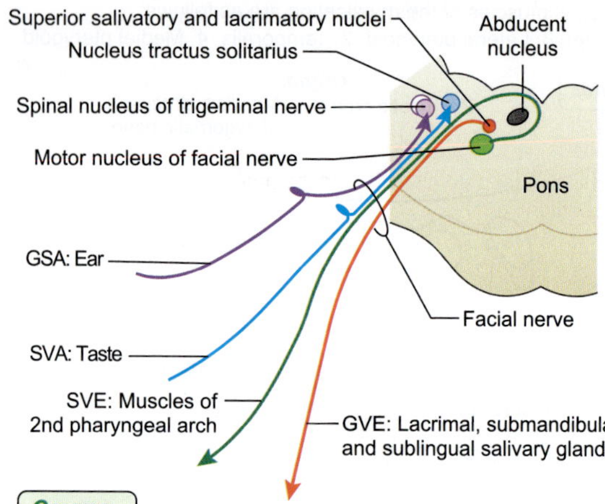

Origin

From brainstem at pontomedullary junction
2 roots: Medial larger motor root;
Lateral small nervus intermedius or sensory root

Course

Pontomedullary junction → Internal acoustic meatus → Facial canal (geniculate ganglion) → Stylomastoid foramen → within parotid gland

Branches

Greater petrosal nerve: Secretomotor fibres to lacrimal, nasal, palatal glands
Nerve to stapedius
Chorda tympani nerve: Parasympathetic to submandibular and sublingual glands
Taste sensation from anterior 2/3rds of tongue except vallate papillae
Posterior auricular nerve: To occipitalis, posterior auricular muscles
Nerve to posterior belly of digastric and stylohyoid
Terminal branches:
1. Temporal
2. Zygomatic
3. Buccal
4. Marginal mandibular
5. Cervical

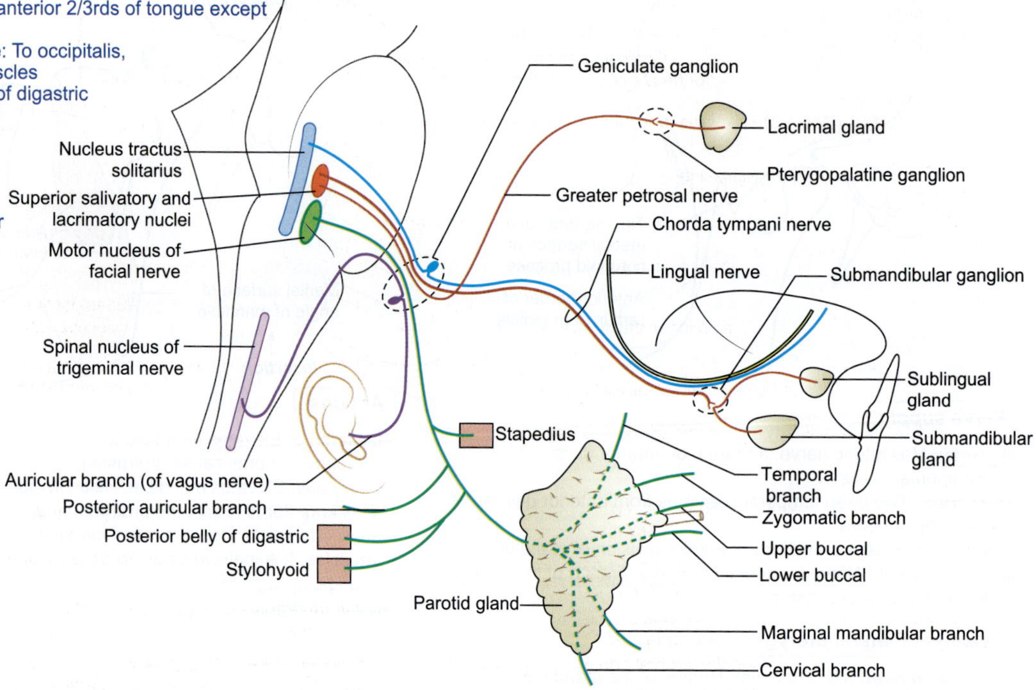

Bell's palsy

Injury to the facial nerve near or outside the stylomastoid foramen produces Bell's palsy.
It is lower motor neuron type of paralysis of muscles of facial expressions.
It may be due to viral infection or unknown cause.

- Unopposed actions of muscles of unaffected side → Facial asymmetry
- Paralysis of occipitofrontalis → Loss of horizontal wrinkles of forehead
- Paralysis of orbicularis oculi → Inability to close the eye; Widening of palpebral fissure; Spilling of tears
- Paralysis of levator labii superioris alaeque nasi → Loss of nasolabial furrow
- Paralysis of orbicularis oris → Drooping of angle of mouth toward affected side; Drooling of saliva
- Paralysis of buccinator → Inability of whistling; Accumulation of food in vestibule of mouth

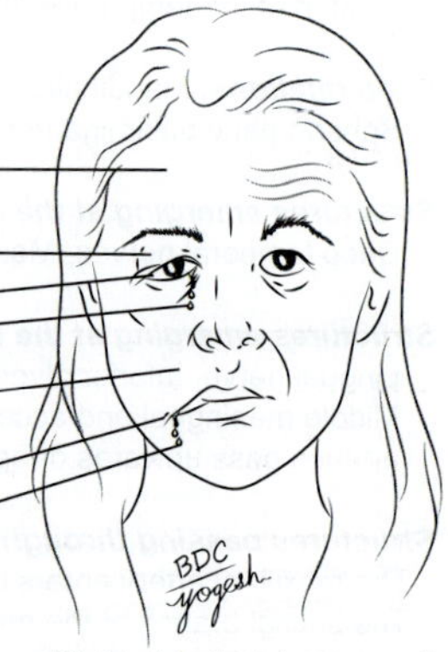

Right side facial nerve palsy

Internal Capsule

A large band of fibres, situated in the inferomedial part of each cerebral hemisphere.

Continuation: Upward as corona radiata; Below as crus cerebri

Relations

Medially: Head of caudate nucleus and thalamus
Laterally: Lentiform nucleus

Parts

V-shaped
Anterior limb, Genu, Posterior limb, Retrolentiform part, Sublentiform part

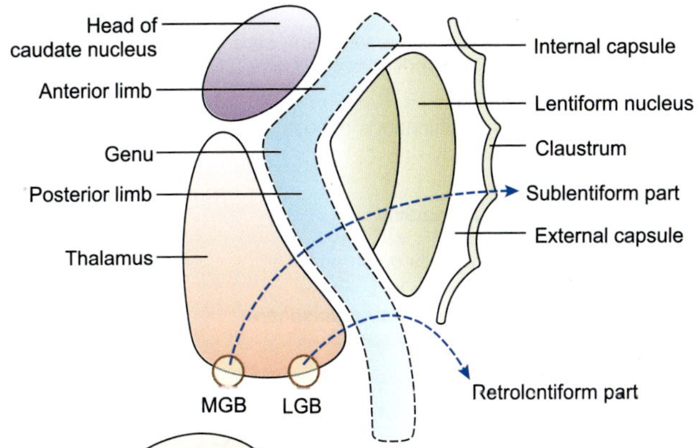

Constituent fibres

Motor

Corticopontine:
Frontopontine, parietopontine, temporopontine, occipitopontine
Pyramidal: Corticonuclear, corticospinal
Extrapyramidal fibres

Sensory

Thalamic radiations:
Anterior, Superior, Inferior, Posterior

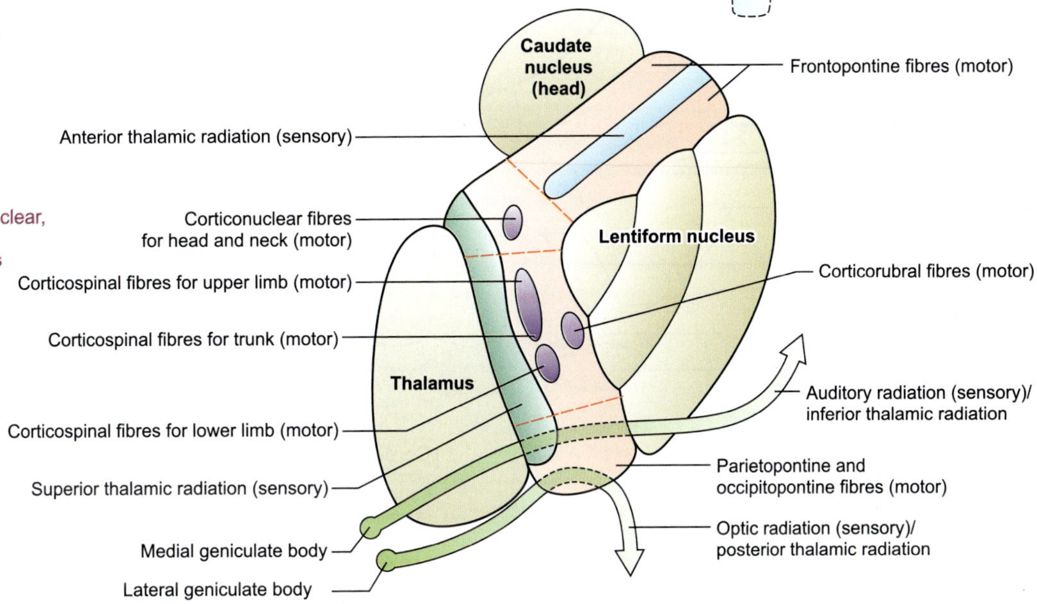

Blood supply

Medial and lateral branches of MCA
Striate branches of ACA
Cortical branches of anterior choroidal artery
Few direct branches from ICA
Central branches of posterior communicating artery
Posterolateral central branches of PCA

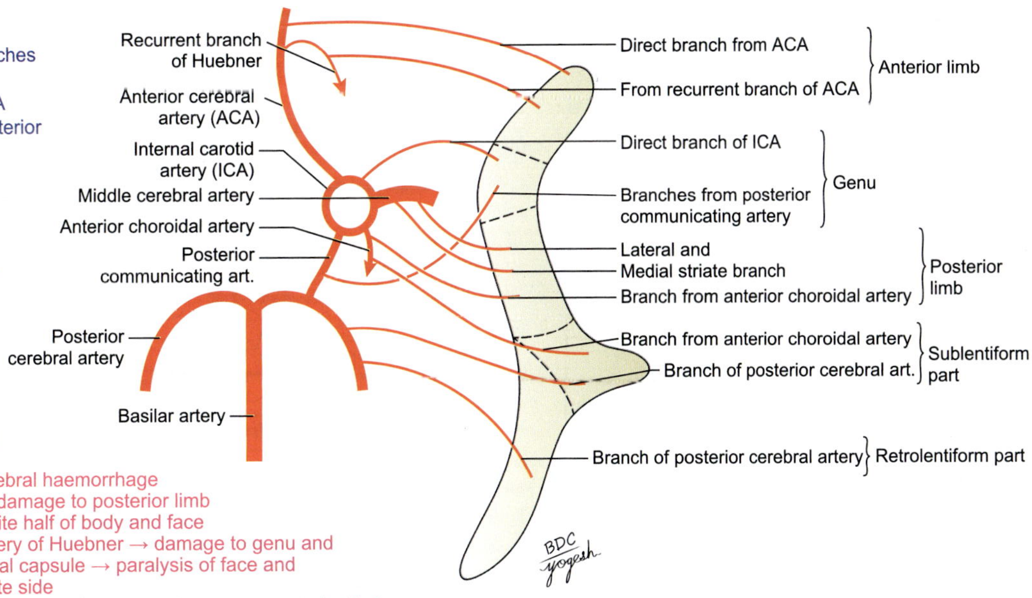

Clinical integration

Lesion of artery of cerebral haemorrhage (Charcot's artery) → damage to posterior limb → paralysis of opposite half of body and face
Lesion of recurrent artery of Huebner → damage to genu and anterior limb of internal capsule → paralysis of face and upper limb on opposite side
Thrombosis of anterior choroidal artery → damage to posterior limb, sublentiform and retrolentiform parts → visual (hemiplegia) and auditory defects

Cerebellum

Part of rhombencephalon, 150 g

Location

Lies in posterior cranial fossa; Below tentorium cerebelli
Behind pons, medulla and 4th ventricle

Functions

Extrapyramidal activities: Maintenance of posture, muscle tone, coordination of fine movements

Cerebellar peduncles

1. Superior – Connects with midbrain
2. Middle – Connects with pons
3. Inferior – Connects with medulla oblongata

External features

Parts: Two cerebellar hemispheres, Median vermis
Surfaces: Superior surface – Convex
Inferior surface: Vallecula – Deep notch
- Sulcus vallecula separates vermis from cerebellar hemispheres

Notches: Anterior: V-shaped, Lodges pons and medulla
Posterior: Deep, Lodges falx cerebelli
Fissure: Horizontal, Posterolateral, Fissura prima
Folia: Leaf-like, lamellae separated by fissures
Lobes: Anterior, Posterior, Flocculonodular lobes

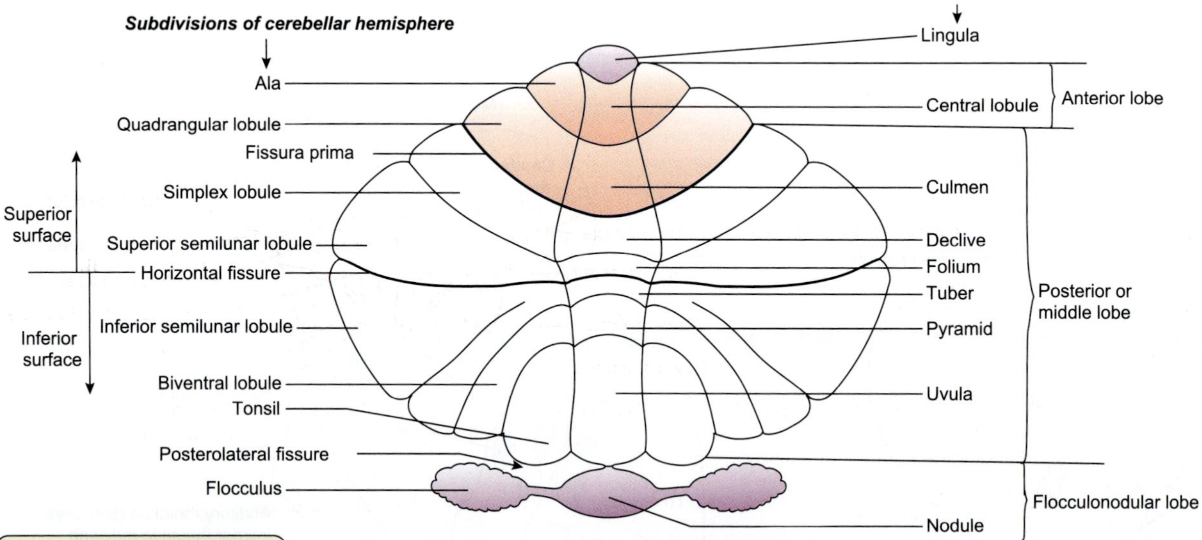

Connections of cerebellum

Inferior cerebellar peduncle

Afferent: Posterior spinocerebellar fibres, Vestibulocerebellar tract Olivocerebellar tract, Par-olivocerebellar tract, Cuneocerebellar fibres, Reticulocerebellar fibre, Anterior external arcuate fibres
Efferent: Cerebelloreticular fibres, Cerebellovestibular fibres, Cerebello-olivary fibres

Middle cerebellar peduncle

Afferent: Pontocerebellar fibres, Reticulocerebellar fibres
Efferent: Nil

Superior cerebellar peduncle

Afferent: Anterior spinocerebellar tract, Tectocerebellar fibres Trigeminocerebellar fibres, Rubrocerebellar fibres Ceruleocerebellar fibres
Efferent: Cerebellorubral fibres, Dentatorubral and dentatothalamic fibres, Cerebello-olivary fibres

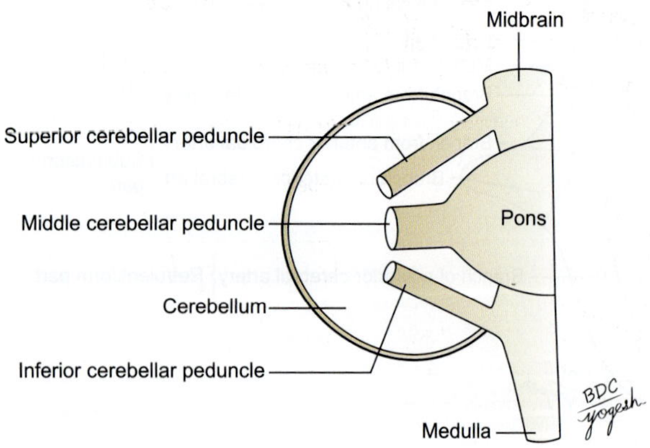

Cerebellar nuclei

Four masses of grey matter embedded deeply in the substance of white matter of cerebellum.

1. Dentate nucleus: Largest cerebellar nucleus, shape like a crumpled purse, it is a nucleus of neocerebellum
2. Emboliform nucleus: Oval, lies lateral to globose nucleus and medial to dentate nucleus.
3. Globose nucleus: Round, lies between emboliform and fastigial nuclei. The emboliform and globose nuclei are part of paleocerebellum. They are collectively called nucleus interpositus.
4. Nucleus fastigii: Lies close to midline in the vermis just dorsal to 4th ventricle, spherical, it is the nucleus of archicerebellum.

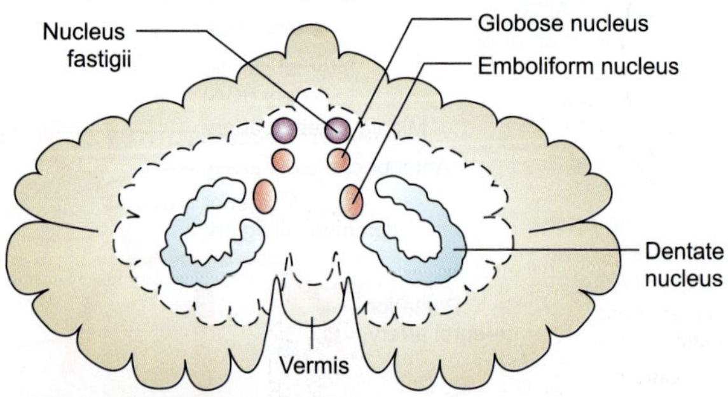

Cerebellar syndrome

Lesion of archicerebellum: Affects trunk muscles, Disequilibrium, Staggering gait, Cerebellar ataxia, Waddling gait, Nystagmus
Lesion of paleocerebellum: Affects limb muscles, Flail joints, Pendular knee jerk, Cerebellar ataxia
Lesion of neocerebellum: Affects skilled movements, Asynergy Dysmetria (finger–nose test), Intention tremors, Dysdiadochokinesia, Adiadochokinesia, Dysarthria/scanning speech, Rebound phenomenon, Hypotonia

Fourth Ventricle

Tent-like cavity of rhombencephalon

Location

Cavity of hindbrain, Lies between cerebellum behind and pons and medulla anteriorly

Continuity

Superiorly – Cerebral aqueduct
Inferiorly – Central canal of medulla

Lateral boundaries

Inferolateral: Gracile and cuneate tubercles, inferior cerebellar peduncles
Superolateral: Superior cerebellar peduncles

Communications

With 3rd ventricle: Cerebral aqueduct
With central canal of medulla:
- Foramen of Magendie,
- Two foramina of Luschka

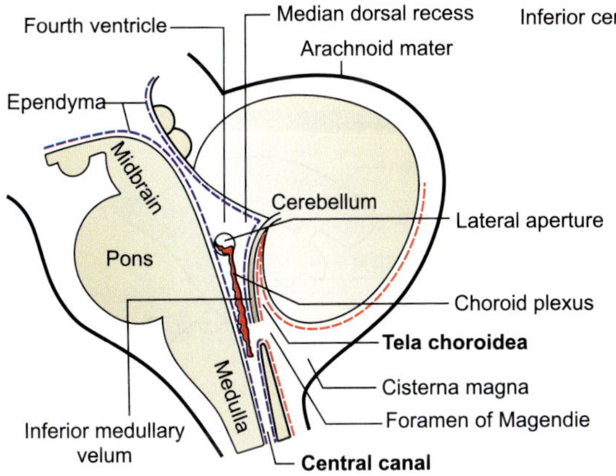

Recesses

Two lateral, Two dorsolateral
One median dorsal

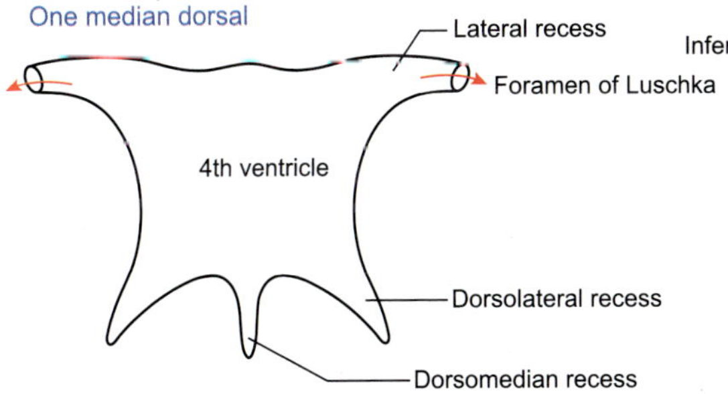

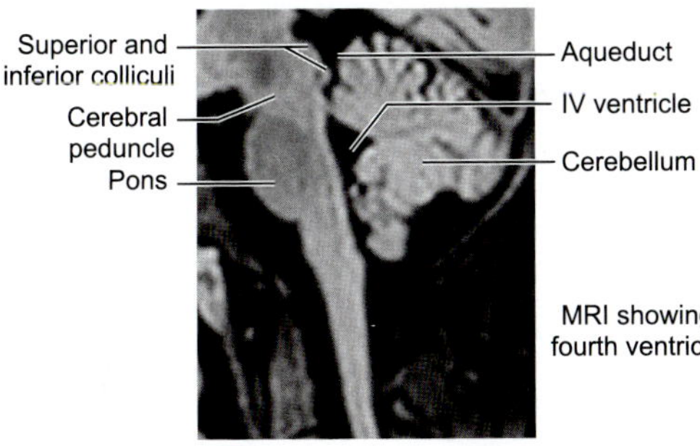

MRI showing fourth ventricle

Floor

Rhomboid fossa

Sulci and depressions

Median sulcus, Median eminence, Sulcus limitans
Superior fovea, Inferior fovea

Areas/structures

Facial colliculus, Locus coeruleus, Hypoglossal triangle
Vagal triangle, Funiculus separans, Area postrema, Taenia, Obex

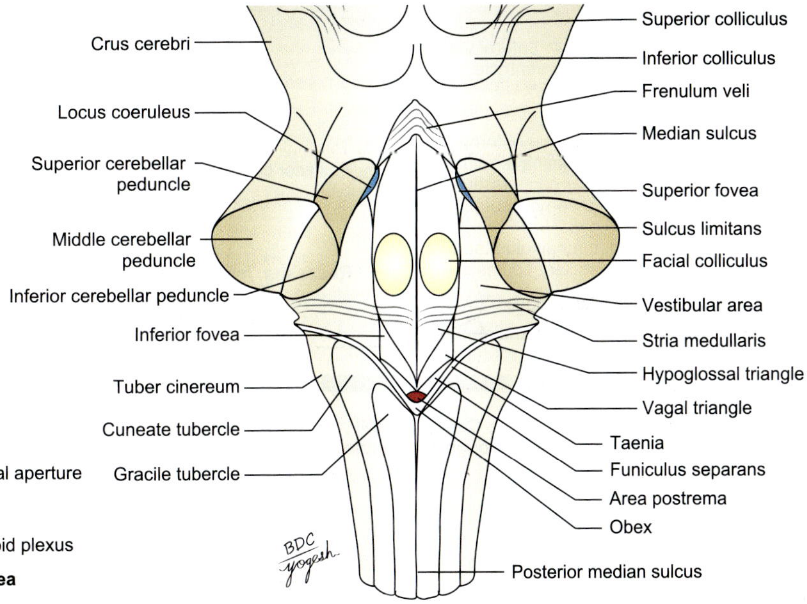

Roof

Tent-shaped
Upper part: Superior medullary velum
Inferior part: Inferior medullary velum, Ependyma and fold of pia mater

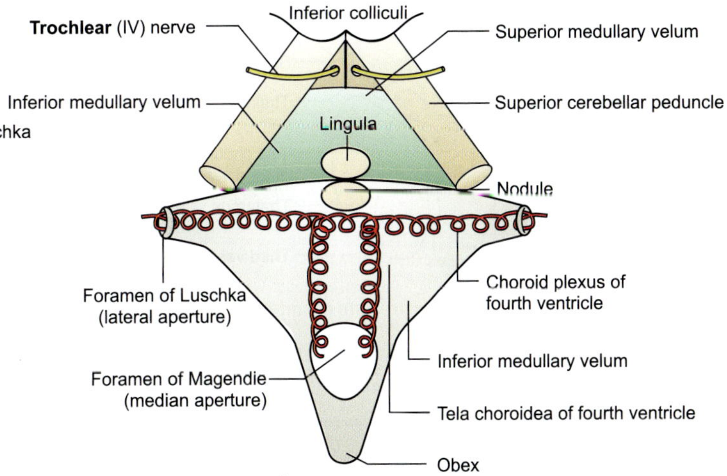

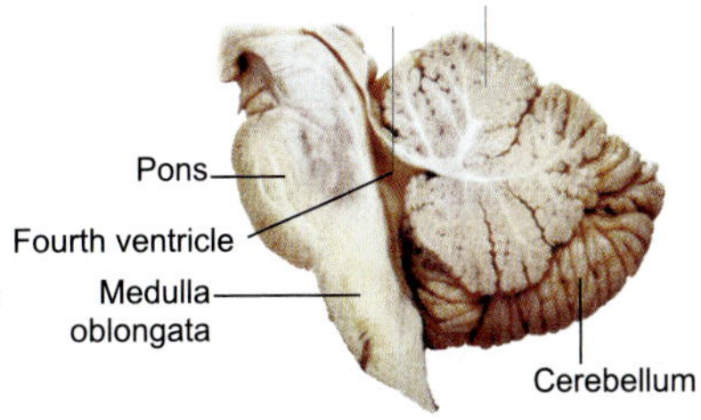

Clinical integration

Blockage of 4th ventricle → hydrocephalus, medulloblastoma, vital centres

Third Ventricle

A median cleft between the two thalami.
Developmentally, represents cavity of diencephalon, except for the area in front of the interventricular foramen which is derived from the median part of the telencephalon.
The cavity is lined by ependyma.

Extent, contents

Extent: From lamina terminalis to cerebral aqueduct
Contents: CSF, Interthalamic adhesion

Communications

Interventricular foramen ↔ Lateral ventricles
Cerebral aqueduct ↔ 4th ventricle

Boundaries

Anterior wall: Anterior column of fornix, Anterior commissure, Lamina terminalis
Posterior wall: Habenular commissure, Pineal gland, Posterior commissure
Roof: Ependymal lining
Floor: Optic chiasma, Infundibulum and tuber cinereum, Mammillary bodies, Posterior perforated substance Tegmentum of midbrain
Lateral walls: Thalamus, Hypothalamus

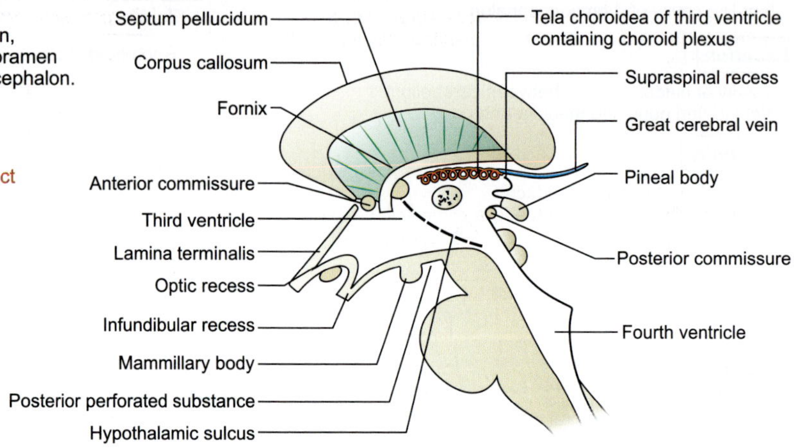

Recesses: Infundibular, Optic, Pineal, Suprapineal

Clinical integration: Obstruction in 3rd ventricle → Increased ICT, endoscopic third ventriculostomy

Lateral Ventricle

C-shaped cavity, Capacity: 7–10 ml, ***Contents:*** CSF, choroid plexus
Communicates with 3rd ventricle through interventricular foramen

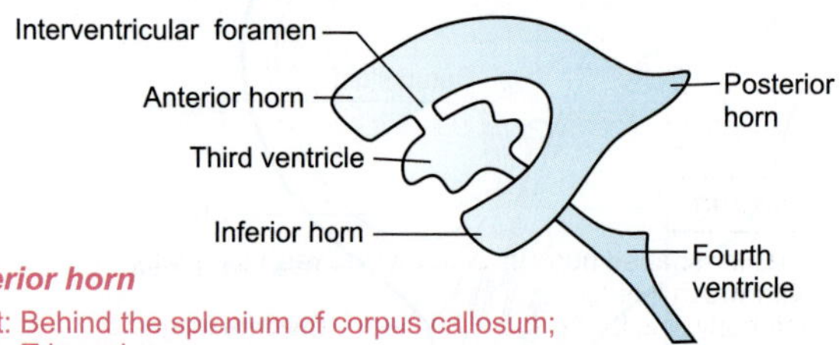

Parts

Body

Extent: From interventricular foramen to splenium; Shape: Triangular
Roof: Corpus callosum
Medial wall: Septum pellucidum
Floor: Caudate nucleus, Stria terminalis, Thalamostriate vein Thalamus, Choroid plexus, Fornix

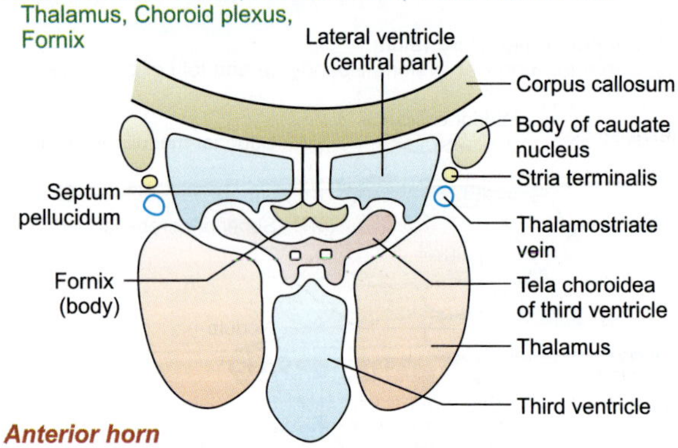

Posterior horn

Extent: Behind the splenium of corpus callosum;
Shape: Triangular
Roof: Tapetum of corpus callosum;
Lateral wall: Tapetum
Medial wall: Bulb of posterior horn, Calcar avis

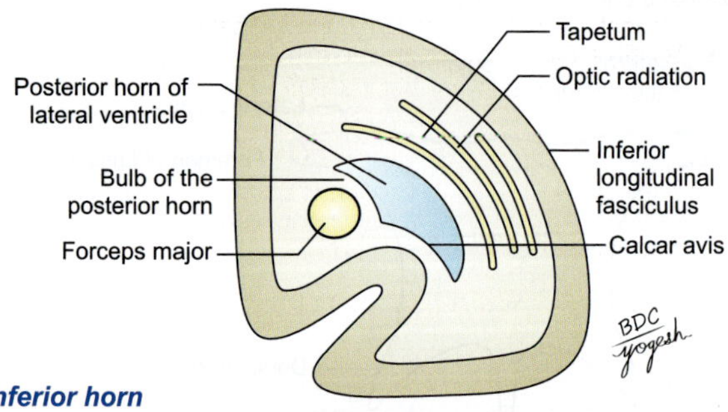

Anterior horn

Extent: From interventricular foramen to genu of corpus callosum
Shape: Triangular
Roof: Body of corpus callosum; Floor: Rostrum, Head of caudate nucleus
Medial wall: Septum pellucidum; Lateral wall: Head of caudate nucleus
Anterior wall: Genu of corpus callosum

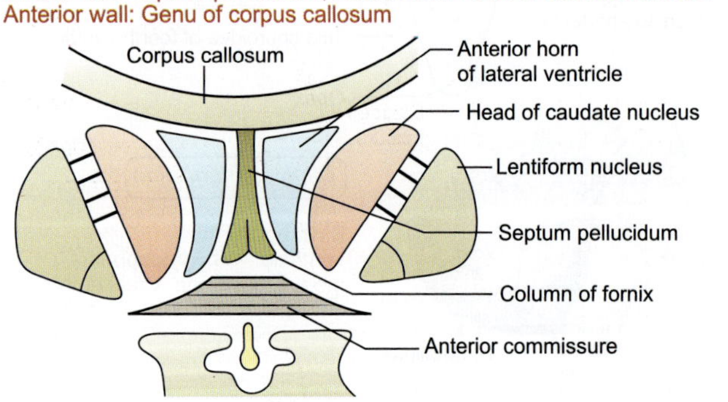

Inferior horn

Extent: Inferiorly in temporal lobe; Shape: Transverse slit
Roof: Tapetum of corpus callosum, Tail of caudate nucleus, stria terminalis, amygdaloid body
Floor: Collateral eminence, Hippocampus with alveus

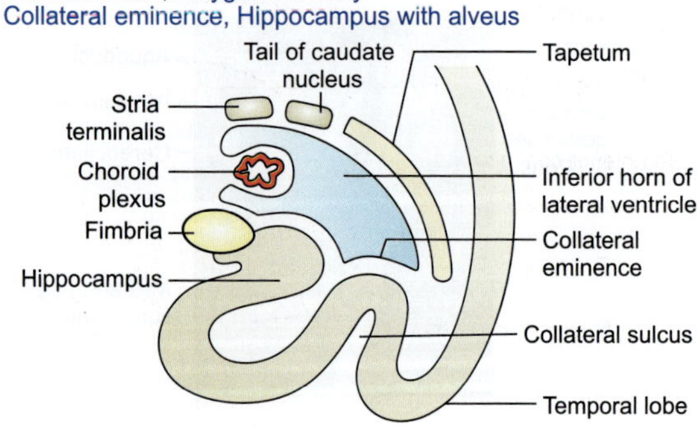

Basal Ganglia

Basal nuclei are subcortical and, intracerebral masses of grey matter forming important parts of extrapyramidal system

Components

Corpus striatum: Caudate nucleus,
Lentiform nucleus: Globus pallidus, Putamen
Claustrum, Amygdaloid body

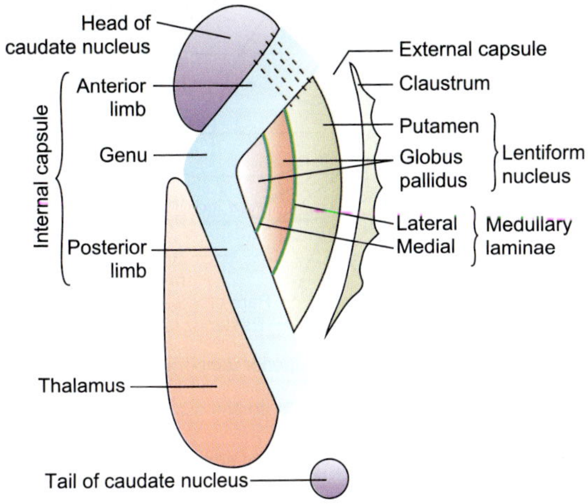

Functions

Corpus striatum: Controls extrapyramidal system
Amygdaloid body: Part of limbic system
Claustrum: Function – not known

Claustrum

Saucer-shaped nucleus situated between the putamen and insula, with which it is coextensive.
Inferiorly, it is thickest and continuous with the anterior perforated substance.

Amygdaloid body

Nuclear mass in temporal lobe, lying anterosuperior to the inferior horn of the lateral ventricle.
Topographically – continuous with the tail of caudate nucleus
Functionally – Related to the stria terminalis
– A part of the limbic system

Afferents: From the olfactory tract.
Efferents: It gives rise to the stria terminalis which ends in the anterior commissure, the anterior perforated substance and in hypothalamic nuclei.

Functions: Emotional control. Controls smell related sexual behaviour.

Damage to amygdaloid body if bilateral causes increase in sexual activity and reduced fear.

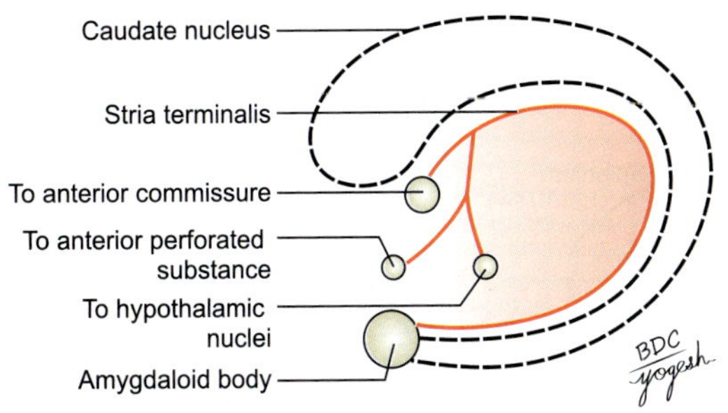

Corpus striatum

Caudate nucleus

C-shaped mass of grey matter
Parts: Head, body, and tail

Lentiform nucleus

Biconvex, lens-shaped mass of grey matter
Parts: Putamen: Large, lateral;
Globus pallidus: Small, medial;
External medullary lamina

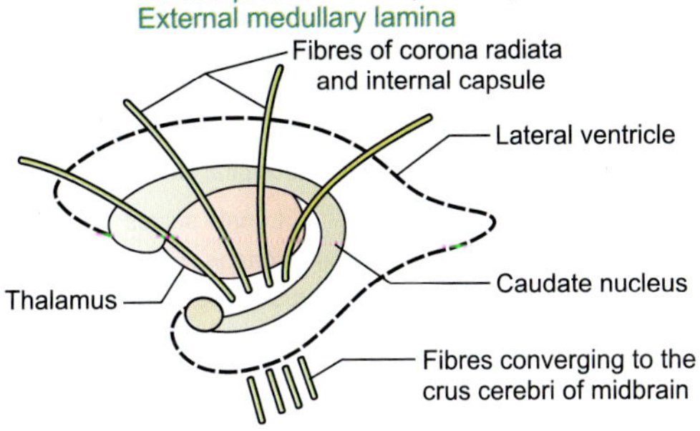

Connections of Corpus Striatum

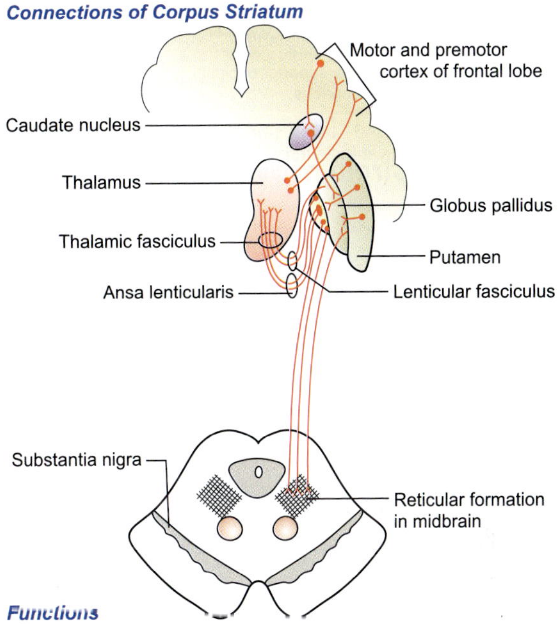

Functions

Refinement of reflex and voluntary, skilled movements
Controls automatic associated movements
Prevents unwanted movements, Maintains muscle tone
Controls emotional expression of movements

Parkinsonism

Group of symptoms including:
bradykinesia, stiffness, tremors

Cause:
Lesion of basal ganglia
→ Deficiency of dopamine
→ Lack of inhibition of corpus striatum →
Extrapyramidal symptoms

Sign and symptoms
Resting tremors, Cog-wheel rigidity
Mask face appearance
Bradykinesia, Pill-rolling movements
Stooped-posture

Treatment
- Levodopa
- Surgical resection of globus pallidus and anterior nucleus of thalamus

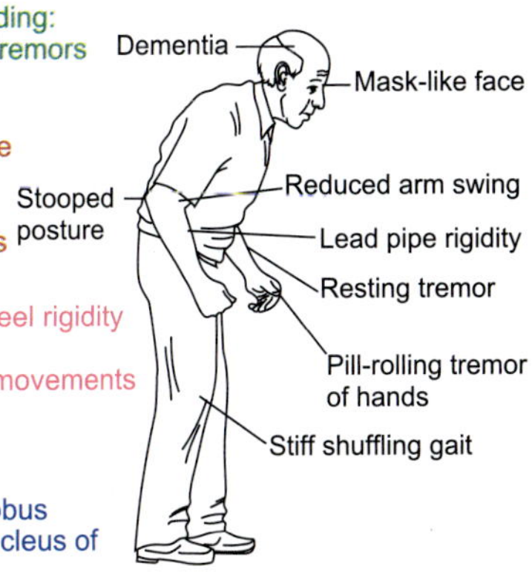

Superolateral Surface of Cerebral Hemisphere

Lobes

Frontal

Sulci: Precentral, superior frontal, inferior frontal, anterior horizontal and anterior ascending rami of lateral sulcus
Gyri: Precentral, superior frontal, middle frontal, inferior frontal, pars orbitalis, pars triangularis, pars opercularis

Parietal

Sulci: Postcentral, Intraparietal
Gyri: Postcentral, superior parietal lobule, inferior parietal lobule, supramarginal, angular, arcus temporo-occipitalis

Temporal

Sulci: Superior temporal, Inferior temporal
Gyri: Superior temporal, middle temporal, inferior temporal

Occipital

Sulci: Transverse occipital, lateral occipital, lunate superior and inferior polar, calcarine
Gyri: Arcus parieto-occipitalis, superior occipital, inferior occipital, gyrus descendens

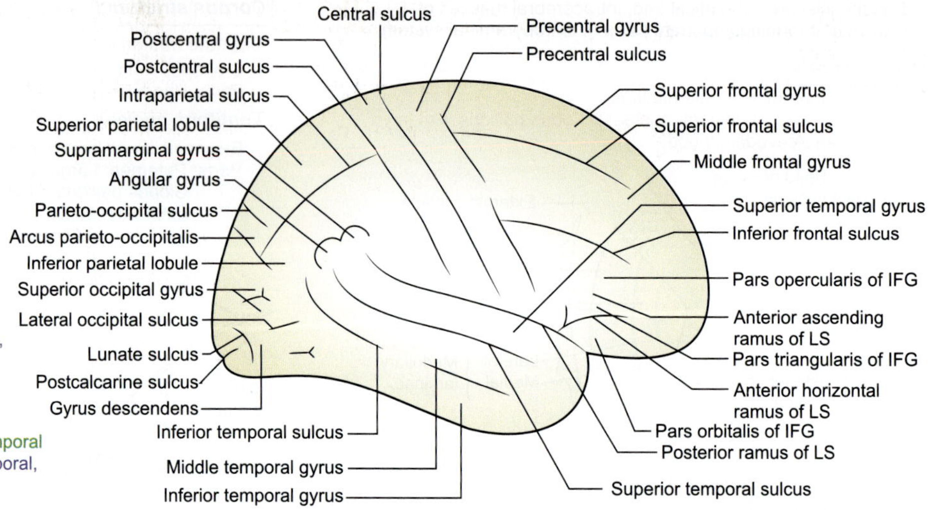

Circle of Willis

Arterial circle
Lies in interpeduncular fossa

Formation

Anteriorly: Anterior communicating
Anterolaterally: Anterior cerebral
Posterolaterally: Posterior communicating
Posteriorly: Posterior cerebral
Posteriorly: Posterior cerebral
Laterally: Internal carotid

Branches

Cortical branches
Central branches : Anteromedial group, Two anterolateral groups
Posteromedial group, Two posterolateral groups
Choroidal branches: Anterior choroidal branch, Posterior choroidal branch

Function

In case of blockade, provide collateral circulation

Clinical integration

Congenital cerebral aneurysm, Berry aneurysm
↓ Rupture
Subarachnoid hemorrhage

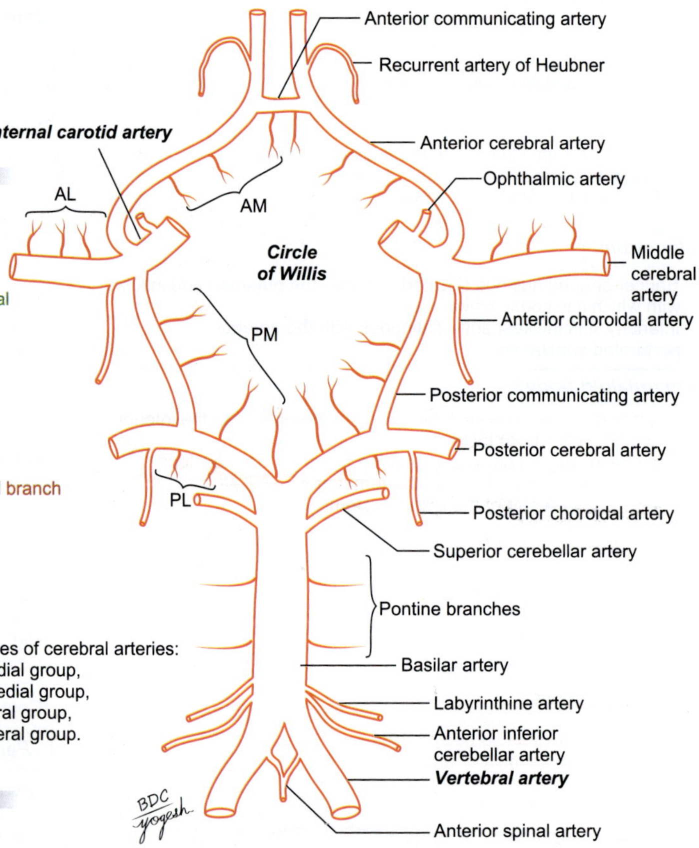

Central branches of cerebral arteries:
AM: Anteromedial group,
PM: Posteromedial group,
AL: Anterolateral group,
PL: Posterolateral group.

Corpus Callosum

Commissural fibres
Connects right and left cerebral hemispheres

Size and shape

L: 10 cm Breadth: 2.5 cm
Connects cerebral hemispheres,
C-shaped, Concave downward

Parts

Rostrum, Genu, Body (trunk), Splenium

Clinical integration

Congenital absence of corpus callosum
↓
Split brain syndrome

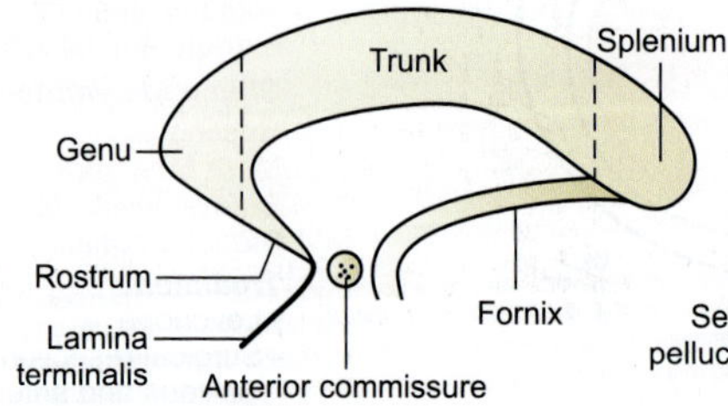

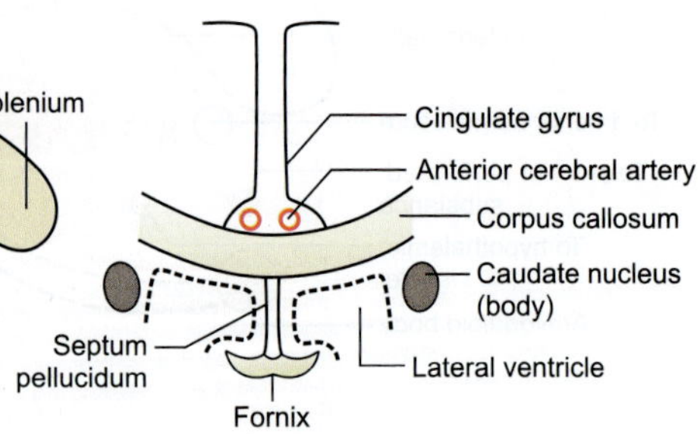